INTERSCIENCE TRACTS ON PHYSICS AND ASTRONOMY

Edited by R. E. Marshak

University of Rochester

Additional volumes in preparation

CONCEPTS IN PHOTOCONDUCTIVITY AND ALLIED PROBLEMS

ALBERT ROSE

RCA Laboratories
Princeton, New Jersey

1963
INTERSCIENCE PUBLISHERS
a division of John Wiley & Sons, New York • London

To L. L. R.

Preface

Photoconductivity is far better understood than the usual cursory treatment in books on solid-state physics would suggest. Along with the improved understanding have come the use of photoconductivity to probe the defect structure of solids and a variety of applications in the form of television camera tubes, electrostatic photography, light amplifiers, electrical switches and an array of simple radiation detectors.

Recently the performance of photoconductors has been cast in a simple and general relation between the sensitivity, speed of response, and conductivity of the photoconductor—called the gain–bandwidth product. This relation has a far-reaching effect on the performance limits to be expected from any devices using photoconductors. It serves also as the rallying point for clear definitions of such concepts as traps, recombination centers, free-carrier lifetime, and response time. The relation makes use of space-charge-limited current flow in solids and hence provides the occasion for treating such current flow problems in this tract along with the effects of electrical contacts on volume currents.

Photoconductivity is a particularly good vantage point from which to view a number of allied fields. The analysis of recombination processes in photoconductors is equally valid for those processes in semiconductor and luminescent materials. The current-gain process in photoconductors is a close equivalent of the current gain in solid-state triodes. The gain–bandwidth product for both photoconductors and solid-state triodes can be traced to and phrased in terms of the phenomenon of space-charge-limited current flow. The exploration of the physics of injected free pairs is enormously facilitated in photoconductors by the universality of optical injection as compared with the highly specialized conditions for electrical injection. Finally, the analysis of noise currents, capture processes, and electrical contacts, while not peculiar to photoconductors, are often more easily explored using photoconductors.

The subject of photoconductivity has seen its most extensive treatment in the volume, *Photoconductivity of Solids*, by R. H. Bube. The goal of the present tract is more restricted and stresses primarily a compact treatment of the concepts and formalisms I have found useful for understanding recombination processes, the interaction between space-charge-limited and photocurrents, the role of electrical contacts, and the noise properties of currents in solids. The references include those publications from which the contents of the chapters were drawn, together with some representative references to papers presenting other points of view. Extensive reference to the literature on photoconductivity will be found in the volume by Bube.

The contents of this tract formed part of a course on "Electronic Processes in Insulators" given in 1961–1962 at the Department of Electrical Engineering at Princeton University. This was a welcome opportunity to try to assemble a number of scattered topics into a related discourse. I am indebted to the members of the seminar and to the members of the staff: G. Warfield, S. Rodriguez, and P. J. Warter, Jr., for numerous critical comments. At the RCA Laboratories (Princeton) where this tract was cultivated over the last two decades, I have had the benefit of repeated discussions and in some cases close collaboration with D. O. North, M. A. Lampert, R. H. Bube, H. S. Sommers, Jr., and R. Williams and at Laboratories RCA, Zurich with F. Stöckmann and W. Ruppel. Finally, I have had the opportunity of interacting with much of the early work on photoconductivity, space-charge-limited currents, and electrical contacts by P. K. Weimer, R. H. Bube, R. W. Smith, S. V. Forgue, A. D. Cope, and R. Williams.

June, 1962   ALBERT ROSE
Princeton, New Jersey

Contents

ix

Chapter 1

General Remarks

The absorption of light by a solid is a quantum process in which electrons are raised to higher energy levels. Ordinarily this leads to a higher conductivity, particularly when electrons are excited from localized states to the conduction band or from a filled (nonconducting) valence band to the conduction band. In this sense, it is not important whether the electrons arrive at the higher energy states by photoexcitation, by cathode ray bombardment,* or by electrical injection. The considerations in this tract apply to all of these processes. The significant questions are the steady-state increases in densities of free carriers and the lifetimes of free carriers by which these increases are determined.

When electrons are excited into the conduction band from the valence band, both free-electron and free-hole densities are built up. The direct recombination of free electrons and free holes is normally a less likely process than their indirect recombination via defect states in the forbidden zone. The latter are usually more numerous and have higher capture cross sections for free carriers. We assume in this tract the existence of defect states in the forbidden zone and make only passing

---

* While electrons are excited by light and electron bombardment to states well above the bottom of the conduction band, they normally settle down to a thermal equilibrium distribution in times of 10^{-9} to 10^{-10} sec that are short compared with the usual lifetime of the excited electron in the conduction band.

reference to their physical and chemical origin. On the one hand, specific chemical impurities and physical imperfections are known to occur with densities of $10^{15}/cm^3$ and greater. A density of defects of $10^{15}/cm^3$ corresponds to a departure from perfection of only one part in 10^8. On the other hand, the response times of photoconductors can easily be affected by defect state densities even lower than $10^{10}/cm^3$. Since there is little or no independent information on such low densities of imperfections, we can assume their presence throughout the forbidden zone of most materials and use the photoconductive process to explore this assumption.

No special distinction is drawn between single crystalline, polycrystalline, and amorphous states or between inorganic and organic materials. As long as excited electrons are more mobile than unexcited electrons, one can expect photocurrents and can analyze the result in terms of a real or effective mobility of the excited carriers. The detailed description of the "conduction band" in amorphous materials may be in some doubt, but the fact that there exist ranges of energies in which electrons are mobile and other ranges in which they are not mobile is in no doubt. In brief, the sheer existence of a band structure—a forbidden zone and a conduction band—may be derived from the proximity of atoms and their atomic properties and does not necessarily require a periodic arrangement of atoms.

The dimensions of the field of photoconductivity are impressive. Photocurrents have been observed in materials having resistivities ranging from less than an ohm-cm to more than 10^{18} ohm-cm. Moreover, photoeffects in the volume of metals and superconductors have been detected. The lifetimes of free carriers, a direct measure of photosensitivities, range from seconds to 10^{-13} seconds. Lifetimes longer than 10^{-4} sec are sufficient to identify a photoconductor as "sensitive" in normal usage. This separation is, of course, somewhat arbitrary and depends on the range of the observer's measuring instruments as well as the range of the observer's interests. Finally, one would have to make an effort to find materials in which photocurrents are not detectable. The last remark is added to temper an attitude common in the early history of photoconductivity, namely, the search for new photoconductors.

References

Reviews

Bube, R. H., *Solid State Physics*, Vol. *11*, Academic Press, New York, 1962, p. 223. Edited by F. Seitz and D. Turnbull.
Rose, A., *RCA Rev.*, *12*, 362 (1951).
Rose, A., *Proc. IRE*, *43*, 1850 (1955).

Books

Breckenridge, R. G., B. R. Russell, and E. E. Hahn, eds., *Photoconductivity Conference*, Wiley, New York–London, 1954.
Bube, R. H., *Photoconductivity of Solids*, Wiley, New York–London, 1960.
Gudden, B., *Lichtelektrische Erscheinungen*, Springer, Berlin, 1928.
Levinstein, H., ed., *Photoconductivity*, Pergamon Press, New York, 1962.
Moss, T. S., *Photoconductivity in the Elements*, Academic, New York, 1952.

Chapter 2

Gain–Bandwidth Product for Photoconductors—Part I

We begin with a short discussion of the maximum product of sensitivity and speed of response that can be achieved with photoconductors. Chronologically, this simple yet powerful relationship came as the culmination of a clearer understanding of the photoconductive process and of space-charge current flow in solids. Hence, one might expect this chapter to appear at the end of the volume. We introduce it here because the argument can be simply stated and because it serves to give both meaning and purpose to a number of the concepts that will be discussed in succeeding chapters.

Consider an insulator of unit cross-sectional area (Fig. 2.1) exposed to a uniform volume excitation which generates free electrons at the *total* rate of F per second. The *total* number of photogenerated free electrons, in the steady state, will be given by

$$\mathfrak{N} = F\tau \tag{2.1}$$

where τ is the lifetime of a free electron. τ counts only the time spent by an electron in the conduction band. If the electron is trapped and thermally re-emitted to the conduction band, the time spent in traps is not included in τ.

The photocurrent will be

$$I = \mathfrak{N}e/T_r \tag{2.2}$$

where T_r is the transit time of a free electron from cathode to

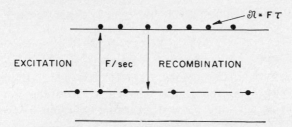

Fig. 2.1. Photoexcitation and recombination.

anode. The cathode is assumed to make "Ohmic" contact to the conduction band. This is the same type of contact that is implicitly assumed when one expects to observe Ohm's law for any ordinary resistor. Its meaning will be discussed at length in Chapter 8. For the present, we take advantage of the common ideas and experience with such contacts.

Equation 2.1 for $\mathfrak{N}$ is inserted into equation 2.2 to give

$$I = eF \frac{\tau}{T_r} \qquad (2.3)$$

$$= eFG \qquad (2.3a)$$

where $G \equiv \tau/T_r$ is the photoconductive gain. It is equal to the number of electrons passing through the photoconductor per excitation or absorbed photon.

We note, in passing, that G can be greater or less than unity and can vary continuously across the value of unity without any change in the physics of the process. A continuous variation of voltage applied to the photoconductor or a continuous variation of electrode spacing can effect this variation of gain. Much of the early literature on photoconductivity assigned a special significance to the value of unity for the gain—much as one might do if he were dealing with a vacuum photocell. As we shall see, this concept of a maximum of one electron per photon requires special electrodes, namely, "blocking" electrodes in contrast to the more normal Ohmic electrodes assumed here.

The transit time is given by

$$T_r = \frac{L}{v_d} = \frac{L}{\mathcal{E}\mu} = \frac{L^2}{V\mu} \tag{2.4}$$

where v_d is the drift velocity, $\mathcal{E}$ the electric field, μ the mobility of free electrons, and L, the spacing of electrodes.

Equation 2.3 may be written, using equation 2.4, as

$$I = e\frac{F\mu\tau}{L^2} V \tag{2.5}$$

From equation 2.5 we conclude that the photocurrent should increase linearly with applied voltage, assuming that neither the lifetime nor the mobility are voltage dependent. We conclude also that, unless some other physical phenomenon intervenes, the photoconductive gain can be made indefinitely large either by increasing the voltage or by decreasing the electrode spacing.

At this point we make the statement (to be demonstrated in Chapter 4) that when the voltage reaches a value given approximately by:

$$VC = \mathfrak{N}e \tag{2.6}$$

a new physical phenomenon does intervene, namely, a space charge of electrons equal in number to the photoexcited electrons is forced into the photoconductor by the applied field. C is the parallel plate capacitance of the electrodes per unit cross-sectional area of sample. Higher voltages increase this space charge proportionately. At and above this voltage, the transit time becomes equal to the dielectric relaxation time of the photoconductor and both decrease with increasing voltage. This equality can be shown by manipulating equation 2.6 as follows:

$$\frac{4\pi VC\mu}{KL} = \frac{4\pi\mathfrak{N}e\mu}{KL} \tag{2.7}$$

If now we invert equation 2.7 and substitute $\dfrac{K}{4\pi L} \times 10^{-12}$

for C, we get*

$$\frac{L^2}{V\mu} = T_r = \frac{K}{4\pi ne\mu} \times 10^{-12} = \tau_{\text{rel}} \qquad (2.8)$$

where τ_{rel} is the dielectric relaxation time and K the dielectric constant.

By virtue of equation 2.8, we can write equation 2.3 for voltages high enough to inject space-charge currents:

$$I = eF \frac{\tau}{\tau_{\text{rel}}} \qquad (2.9)$$

or

$$\frac{I}{eF} \cdot \frac{1}{\tau} = \frac{1}{\tau_{\text{rel}}} \qquad (2.10)$$

Since $I/eF = G$ and since $1/2\pi\tau \doteq \Delta B$, where ΔB is the equivalent amplifier passband for a response time of τ, equation 2.10 may be written

$$G\Delta B = \frac{1}{2\pi\tau_{\text{rel}}} \qquad (2.11)$$

The product $G\Delta B$ is the gain–bandwidth product for the photoconductor considered as a current amplifier and under the condition of space charge-limited flow. Note that τ_{rel} is the relaxation time under the conditions of use. For relatively insulating materials used at low lights, $1/2\pi\tau_{\text{rel}}$ decreases to unity or less. This means that high-gain photoconductors must become very sluggish in response.

Equation 2.11 has been derived for the case of free carriers and no traps. If we now introduce a set of shallow traps in thermal equilibrium with the conduction band such that there are $\mathfrak{N}_t$ total trapped electrons and $\mathfrak{N}_t \gg \mathfrak{N}$, the total number of free electrons, two consequences follow. The response time

---

* Practical units are used here together with the approximation: one farad $\equiv 8.99 \times 10^{11}$ esu $\doteq 10^{12}$ esu.

is increased by the factor $\mathfrak{N}_t/\mathfrak{N}$, since a doubling of the number of free carriers entails a doubling also of the number of trapped carriers. The second consequence is that the voltage at which space-charge currents set in is increased by the factor $\mathfrak{N}_t/\mathfrak{N}$, since a doubling of the free carriers by injected charge must also double the trapped carriers. These two relations are

$$\tau_0 \equiv \text{Response time} = \mathfrak{N}_t/\mathfrak{N}\tau \qquad (2.12)$$

$$T_r = (\mathfrak{N}/\mathfrak{N}_t)\tau_{\text{rel}} \qquad (2.13)$$

We insert equations 2.12 and 2.13 into equation 2.3 to obtain

$$I = eF\,\frac{\tau_0}{\tau_{\text{rel}}} \qquad (2.14)$$

or, as before (eq. 2.11):

$$G\Delta B = \frac{1}{2\pi\tau_{\text{rel}}} \qquad (2.15)$$

We see that, since equations 2.15 and 2.11 are identical, the introduction of shallow traps has not altered the gain–bandwidth product. The reason for the invariance is that the introduction of traps had two opposing effects: increase of response time and increase of voltage at which space-charge currents set in. If we wish to improve the gain–bandwidth product we must look for a way of increasing the voltage at which space-charge currents set in without an increase (or at least as much of an increase) in response time. This can be done in several ways, one of which is illustrated in Figure 2.2.

Here the recombination centers lie at the Fermi level and exceed the number of electrons in trapping states. If we wish to double the free-electron density by injection of space charge, we must also fill most of the empty recombination centers, since a doubling of the free-electron density means that the Fermi level is raised by approximately kT. Hence, space-charge currents will not set in until the applied voltage is sufficient to fill these recombination centers, that is, until

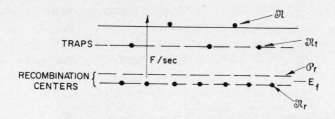

Fig. 2.2. Arrangement leading to $M > 1$.

$$VC = \mathscr{P}_r e \qquad (2.16)$$

Meantime, the introduction of recombination centers has not affected the ratio of response time to lifetime which is still controlled by the relation

$$\tau_0 = (\mathscr{N}_t/\mathscr{N})\tau \qquad (2.17)$$

We see from equations 2.16 and 2.17 that the voltage at which space-charge flow sets in has been increased over that for free carriers alone by the factor $\mathscr{P}_r/\mathscr{N}$, while the factor by which the response time has been increased is only $\mathscr{N}_t/\mathscr{N}$. The increased voltage gives an increased gain and the increased response time gives a decreased bandwidth. Hence, the net advantage of introducing empty recombination centers is

$$1 + \mathscr{P}_r/\mathscr{N}_t \equiv M \qquad (2.18)$$

That is, the maximum gain–bandwidth product of equation 2.11 may now be written

$$G\Delta B = \frac{1}{2\pi\tau_{\mathrm{rel}}} M \qquad (2.19)$$

where $M \geq 1$ and represents in this case unity plus the ratio of empty recombination centers to the number of trapped electrons.

There are other ways by which values of M greater than unity can be achieved and these will be discussed in Chapter 5. It is sufficient here to note that equations 2.18 and 2.19 require a clear distinction between states that are labeled traps and those that are labeled recombination centers. Further, equations 2.10 and 2.14 point up the role of four characteristic times:

τ: lifetime of a free carrier
τ_0: response time of photoconductor
T_r: transit time of a free carrier
τ_{rel}: dielectric relaxation time

Much of the discussion of the following three chapters will be concerned with the understanding of traps, recombination centers, and the four characteristic times.

References

Redington, R. W., *J. Appl. Phys.*, **29**, 189 (1958).

Rose, A., *Helv. Phys. Acta*, **30**, 242 (1957).

Rose, A., and M. A. Lampert, *Phys. Rev.*, **113**, 1227 (1959).

Rose, A., and M. A. Lampert, *RCA Rev.*, **20**, 57 (1959).

Smith, R. W., *Phys. Rev.*, **97**, 1525 (1955).

Stöckmann, F., in R. G. Breckenridge, B. R. Russell, and E. E. Hahn, eds., *Photoconductivity Conference*, Wiley, New York–London, 1954, p. 269.

Stöckmann, F., *Z. Physik*, **147**, 544 (1957).

Chapter 3

Recombination

The total number of photoexcited carriers is given by equation 2.1 in the form

$$\mathfrak{N} = F\tau \qquad (3.1)$$

The photocurrent is derived from equation 3.1 by dividing by the transit time. But the transit time can be adjusted arbitrarily to have almost any desired value by choosing appropriate values of the macroscopic parameters, voltage and electrode spacing. The transit time is not a specific or differentiating property of a photoconductor. The total rate of photoexcitation, F, is also not a characteristic parameter of the photoconductor. In many cases F can be set equal to the incident flux of photons. This is particularly true for strongly absorbed light. The remaining parameter τ, the lifetime of a free carrier, is, then, the characteristic parameter in that it is derived from the particular set of defect states present in the forbidden zone of the photoconductor. This is not to say that τ is a constant for a given chemical compound or even a given sample of that compound. Quite the contrary. τ can depend upon the level of excitation and also upon the absolute temperature. Moreover, variations in material preparation can yield a range of values for τ extending, as it does for CdS, from 10^{-2} to 10^{-10} sec.

A complete discussion of the recombination processes that determine the lifetime of a free carrier is undoubtedly a volume in itself. The treatment given here is one which the writer has found helpful in visualizing a variety of patterns of recombina-

11

tion behavior without resort to elaborate analytic solutions. The latter are likely to contain at least eight parameters and to be not readily suggestive of the underlying physical processes. The emphasis in the present treatment is on a small number of physical concepts that can be used as tools for dissecting a wide range of problems encountered in real materials. The emphasis also is on a division of the array of recombination problems into groups or into ranges of parameters such that simple solutions can be obtained by making approximations prior to mathematical analysis. The exercises in algebra are thereby considerably reduced.

It goes without saying that the study of recombination processes is at the heart not only of photoconductivity, but of luminescence and many semiconductor devices as well. Thus, both insulators and semiconductors need to be considered. Often the solution to the insulator problem gives a more general perspective from which the solution to the semiconductor problem can be readily deduced as a special case.

The recombination models selected for discussion were chosen to be representative of the major patterns of experimental data already encountered in photoconductive insulators and semiconductors.

Insulators

In many applications of photoconductors, the object is to detect small amounts of radiation. It is accordingly desirable to reduce the background of thermally generated carriers to a minimum. Hence, much of the interest in photoconductors is directed towards relatively insulating materials.

We define the area of insulator problems to be those in which the thermally generated densities of carriers are negligible in comparison with the photogenerated densities. At room temperature this means that the forbidden gap should be larger than about 1.5 volts. At lower absolute temperatures, the forbidden gap can be reduced in proportion. This does not mean that a large forbidden gap automatically insures that the material is in the insulator class. Rather, the additional condition should be satisfied that the Fermi level be at least about 0.75 volts from either band edge. The density of carriers corresponding to a Fermi level at 0.75 volts from a band edge is about $10^6/cm^3$ at room temperature.

A set of models has been chosen to lead stepwise to the case of real insulators having a distribution of states throughout the forbidden zone. The first six sections emphasize the facts that the lifetimes of electrons and holes are generally independent of each other; that these two lifetimes may approach equality under conditions of high excitation or extreme purity of material, conditions that are generally assumed to hold for transistor materials; that lifetimes are controlled by recombination centers and response times by the combined effects of recombination centers and traps; that the distinction between traps and recombination centers depends in large part on the statistics of recombination and may shift with the temperature and level of excitation; and that the temperature dependence of photoconductivity has little or no connection with the temperature dependence of the conductivity in the dark.

3.1 Single Set of Recombination Centers $(n, p < n_r, p_r)$ [Low Light]

Consider a set of recombination centers lying near the Fermi level (Fig. 3.1). For definiteness, let their density be $10^{16}/cm^3$ and let p_r be the density of centers unoccupied by electrons and n_r the density of centers occupied by electrons. Let s_n be the capture cross section of an unoccupied center for free electrons and s_p the capture cross section of an occupied center for free holes. Let the material be exposed to light whose energy is somewhat larger than that of the forbidden zone. The volume rate of generation of free electrons *and* free holes is designated by f. We assume further that the densities n and p of excited carriers are both small in comparison with n_r and p_r.

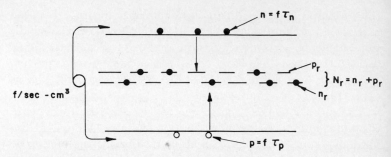

Fig. 3.1. Single set of recombination centers n, $p < n_r$, p_r.

With these assumptions, we can write out of hand

$$n = f\tau_n = \frac{f}{p_r v s_n} \tag{3.1}$$

$$p = f\tau_p = \frac{f}{n_r v s_p} \tag{3.2}$$

For simplicity we are assuming that the thermal velocities v of free electrons and of free holes are equal.

We note that the lifetime of a free electron

$$\tau_n = \frac{1}{p_r v s_n} \tag{3.3}$$

is independent of and, consequently, in general not equal to the lifetime of a free hole

$$\tau_p = \frac{1}{n_r v s_p} \tag{3.4}$$

These expressions for lifetime are derived from the concept that in the time, τ_n, an electron to which the cross-sectional disk, s_n, is attached will trace out a volume $\tau_n v s_n$ equal to the volume p_r^{-1} associated with a capturing center. The concept is valid, providing the mean free path of the electron is larger than the diameter of the cross-sectional disk. For smaller mean free paths, the randomly oriented elements of volume traced out by the electron begin to overlap. The mean free path should also be greater than about half the spacing between capturing centers. For smaller mean free paths, the electron, on the average, must diffuse to the capturing center and its lifetime is increased by a factor of the order of the ratio of half the spacing of centers to the mean free path (see Chapter 7).

The lifetimes τ_n and τ_p can be written out of hand because the assumption of free-carrier densities small compared with recombination center densities means that the occupancy of the recombination centers is *substantially the same after illumination as it was in the dark*. Only the difference $n - p$ can perturb the occupancy of the recombination centers and this difference is by assumption small compared with the density of recombination centers. This is a powerful simplification since it covers a wide range of insulator problems. Recombination state densities are usually greater than $10^{15}/\text{cm}^3$ and photoexcited carrier densities are usually far less than $10^{15}/\text{cm}^3$.

We can, for example, conclude that the lifetimes are constant in the range of carrier densities from about $10^6/\text{cm}^3$ (i.e., the upper limit of densities assumed for thermal carriers) to about $10^{16}/\text{cm}^3$, the density of recombination centers. Further, except for the slow dependency of thermal velocity on temperature, the lifetimes should be insensitive to temperature if the capture cross sections are temperature insensitive.

In the present model we have not yet introduced trapping states. Hence, the response time of the photoconductor will be equal to the lifetime of its majority carrier. The response time is the time for the photocurrent to reach a steady state (or some appropriate fraction of steady state, like 0.5) after initiation of the light. This is also the time required for the photocurrent to decay to the same fraction of its steady-state value after the light is interrupted. If we were to follow the photocurrent down close to the thermal equilibrium value of current, we would find a low long-lived tail slightly in excess of the dark current. This comes about because the electrons in the recombination centers were initially confined to the bottom fraction of recombination centers and were then homogenized or uniformly distributed amongst all the recombination centers by the action of the light and the recombination processes. After removal of the light and after most of the photocurrent has decayed, the electron distribution in the recombination states will still be "hotter" (at an effectively higher temperature) than the ambient and will give rise to a small current until the distribution settles into thermal equilibrium via thermal excitation into the free bands and subsequent recapture.

The states p_r and n_r are called recombination states because a free electron captured into one of the p_r states (thereby converting it to one of the n_r states) will capture a free hole before it is thermally reexcited into the conduction band. Similarly, a free hole captured into one of the n_r states (thereby converting it into one of the p_r states) will capture a free electron before it is thermally reexcited into the valence band. We note that even though, from the point of view of an individual center, the complete recombination act is a two-step process whereby it first captures an electron and then a hole (or vice versa), from the point of the free electrons and holes, their recombination traffics are statistically independent as are, naturally, their lifetimes.

3.2 Single Set of Recombination Centers $(n, p > n_r, p_r)$ [High Light]

In Figure 3.2, a single set of recombination centers is shown

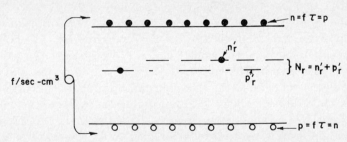

Fig. 3.2. Single set of recombination centers $n, p > n_r, p_r$.

similar in all respects to those in Figure 3.1 except that the density of the centers is low enough, say $10^{12}/\text{cm}^3$, to be exceeded by the optically excited densities of free carriers. Under these conditions, the free-electron and free-hole densities must be closely equal, since any difference $n - p$ must be taken up by the change in occupancy of the recombination centers and the latter density is, by assumption, small compared with n and p. Hence $\tau_n = \tau_p$. It is clear that the occupancy of the recombination centers is modified from n_r, p_r to n_r', p_r' to fit the condition

$$n \doteq p \tag{3.5}$$

or

$$\frac{f}{p_r'vs_n} \doteq \frac{f}{n_r'vs_p} \tag{3.6}$$

From equation 3.6, the new occupancy is given by

$$\frac{n_r'}{p_r'} = \frac{s_n}{s_p} \tag{3.7}$$

or

$$\frac{n_r'}{n_r' + p_r'} = \frac{n_r'}{N_r} = \frac{s_n}{s_n + s_p} \tag{3.8}$$

From equation 3.8 we can write

$$\tau_n = \tau_p = \frac{1}{n_r'vs_p} = \frac{1}{N_rv[s_ps_n/(s_n + s_p)]} \tag{3.9}$$

$$= \frac{1}{N_rvs_n} \quad \text{for } s_n \ll s_p \tag{3.10}$$

or

$$= \frac{1}{N_rvs_p} \quad \text{for } s_p \ll s_n \tag{3.11}$$

Equations 3.10 and 3.11 show that the rate of recombination is controlled by the smaller of the two cross sections. For example, if the capture cross section for electrons, s_n, is small compared with s_p, the recombination states are mostly unoccupied— hence equation 3.10.

In the previous case (Sect. 3.1) of n, $p < n_r$, p_r, the n_r and p_r are taken as fixed and the values of n and p are made to fit. In the present case of n, $p > n_r$, p_r, the necessary equality of n and p forces n_r and p_r to be modified to n_r' and p_r' to make a fit. In the present case as in the previous one, the lifetime is invariant with light intensity, is insensitive to temperature, and is equal to the response time of the photoconductor.

3.3   Single Set of Recombination Centers and of Traps ($n + n_t$, $p + p_t < n_r$, p_r) [Low Light]

The model in Figure 3.3 is the same as that in Figure 3.1, except that a level of electron-trapping states and a level of hole-trapping states have been added. The trapping states are characterized by the fact that a free electron captured into an unoccupied trap will be thermally reexcited into the conduction band before capturing a free hole. Similarly, a free hole captured into a hole trap (occupied by an electron) will be thermally reexcited to the valence band before capturing a free electron. The electron trapping states are in "thermal contact" with the

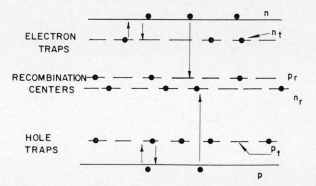

Fig. 3.3. Single level of traps. $n + n_t$, $p + p_t < n_r$, p_r; $n < n_t$; $p < p_t$.

conduction band. This means that their occupancy is related to that in the conduction band by the Boltzmann factor.

$$\exp \frac{\left| E_{tn}, E_c \right|}{kT}$$

In particular,

$$n_t/N_t = n/N_c \exp \frac{\left| E_{tn}, E_c \right|}{kT}$$

or

$$n_t = n(N_t/N_c) \exp \frac{\left| E_{tn}, E_c \right|}{kT} \tag{3.12}$$

N_c is the effective density of states in the conduction band

$$N_c = 2 \left(\frac{2\pi m^* kT}{h^2} \right)^{3/2} \doteq 10^{19}/\text{cm}^3 \text{ for } m^* = m \text{ at } T = 300°\text{K}.$$

N_c is approximately the number of states in the bottom kT slice of the conduction band.

The notation $\left| E_{tn}, E_c \right|$ means the absolute value of the energy interval between E_{tn} and E_c. This notation is used throughout to avoid ambiguity either about the sign of the exponential or the location of the zero reference level of energy.

Similarly,

$$p_t = p(P_t/N_v) \exp \frac{\left| E_{tp}, E_v \right|}{kT} \tag{3.13}$$

where N_v is the effective density of states in the valence band and P_t is the density of hole-trapping states.

Again, we argue as in Section 3.1 that as long as $n + n_t$ and $p + p_t$ are less than n_r and p_r we can take the latter as fixed and having the same values after illumination as before. We can write, by inspection, as in Section 3.1,

$$n = f\tau_n = \frac{f}{p_r v s_n} \tag{3.14}$$

and

$$p = f\tau_p = \frac{f}{n_r v s_p} \qquad (3.15)$$

where f is the number of electron–hole pairs excited per cubic centimeter per second.

The lifetimes τ_n and τ_p are invariant with light intensity and insensitive to temperature. The new element that has been added is the fact that the response time is now no longer equal to the lifetime, but is greater than the lifetime by the factor $(1 + n_t/n)$ for electrons and $(1 + p_t/p)$ for holes. We designate the response times by τ_{0n} and τ_{0p}. Since the response time is dominated by the majority carrier (the carrier with the longer lifetime), the response time associated with the majority carrier will dominate an actual experiment.

The response time is larger than the lifetime because the excitation must now pour electrons into trapping states as well as into the conduction band. For example, suppose that we wish to double the number of free electrons by an increase in light intensity. This means that we must also double the number of electrons in traps. Hence, an additional time, $(n_t/n)\tau_n$, is required to excite enough electrons to double the number of trapped electrons and the total response time is

$$\tau_{0n} = \left(1 + \frac{n_t}{n}\right)\tau_n \qquad (3.16)$$

On interruption of the light we must now wait not only for the free electrons to be captured into the recombination states but also for the trapped electrons to be emptied into the recombination states *via thermal excitation into the conduction band and subsequent capture.* Hence the decay time for the photocurrent will be increased by the same factor as in equation 3.16. The trapped electrons do not have direct access to the recombination states because the discrete states in the forbidden zone lie at physically different places and more than a few lattice spacings removed from each other.

The response times, like the lifetimes, are invariant with light intensity. However, from equations 3.12 and 3.16, the response times approach the lifetimes at higher temperatures at the rate $\exp \left[\left| E_{tn}, E_c \right| / kT \right]$ for electrons and $\exp \left[\left| E_{tp}, E_v \right| / kT \right]$ for holes.

The concept of a response time different from and longer than the lifetime is a very powerful aid in resolving much of the experience with insulating photoconductors. One normally expects the response time to be equal to the lifetime in any excitation process. Accordingly, one would expect the insensitive photoconductors to be particularly fast. Common experience with such photoconductors, however, lends no support to this expectation. Relatively insulating photoconductors, for which lifetimes of less than millimicroseconds can be estimated from their gross insensitivity, have response times of seconds or minutes or even longer. Such experience is readily understood in terms of ratios of trapped to free carriers in the order of 10^{10} and, hence, response times correspondingly longer than lifetimes. A ratio of 10^{10} is consistent with free-carrier densities of $10^5/\text{cm}^3$ and deep-lying trap densities of $10^{15}/\text{cm}^3$. In Section 3.9 it will be shown, in fact, that for certain reasonable trap distributions the response times for photoconductors for a fixed light intensity is approximately independent of the photo-sensitivity.

The above argument has assumed that the trapping time was shorter (by at least a factor of 2) than the recombination time. This is the condition for "thermal contact" between trapped and free carriers. It is easily satisfied by sensitive photoconductors where the recombination time is, by definition, long and in the neighborhood of milliseconds while the trapping time is likely to be microseconds or shorter. In the case of insensitive photoconductors, however, where lifetimes of millimicroseconds are encountered, the trapping time may exceed the lifetime. If the trapping time does exceed the lifetime by more than several fold, the response time approaches closely the lifetime of free carriers. That is, the material acts to changes in light intensity like a trap-free material. Consider, for example, the decay of free carriers on removal of the excitation. If the rate of generation from traps is a tenth the rate of recombination of free carriers into recombination centers, the free carrier density will drop to a tenth its initial value before replenishment from traps begins to keep pace with it. The first 90 per cent drop in free carrier density is as rapid as in a trap-free material. The remainder of the drop will be trap-controlled.

3.4 Single Set of Recombination Centers and of Traps $(n + n_t, p + p_t > n_r, p_r)$ [High Light]

The arguments of Section 3.2 hold for the present model, as well, and lead to the conclusions

$$\tau_n = \tau_p = \frac{1}{N_r v[s_p s_n/(s_n + s_p)]} \qquad (3.17)$$

Also, by the same arguments as in Section 3.3, the response times are

$$\tau_{0n} = \tau_n \left(1 + \frac{n_t}{n}\right) \qquad (3.18)$$

and

$$\tau_{0p} = \tau_p \left(1 + \frac{p_t}{p}\right) \qquad (3.19)$$

The response times are invariant with light intensity and approach the common lifetime at increasing temperature at the respective rates exp $[\,|\,E_{tn},\ E_c\,|/kT\,]$ for electrons and exp $[\,|\,E_{tp},\ E\,|/kT\,]$ for holes.

3.5 Transition Range $(n_r > n + n_t > p_r;\ n + n_t > p + p_t)$

In the previous sections we have discussed the limiting cases of free-plus-trapped carriers small compared with recombination center densities at the one extreme and large compared with

recombination center densities at the other. The transition between these two limits is characterized by a set of interlaced
inequalities such that, for example, the density of free-plus-
trapped electrons is larger than the density of unoccupied
recombination centers but smaller than the density of occupied
centers, and the density of free-plus-trapped holes is small
compared with the density of free-plus-trapped electrons. Let
the electrons also be the majority carriers. Hence the difference
$(n + n_t) - (p + p_t)$ must appear as new unoccupied recombination centers in order to satisfy the condition of charge
neutrality.

Let the modified density of unoccupied recombination centers
be p_r'. Then the following approximations are valid:

$$(n + n_t) - (p + p_t) \doteq n + n_t \doteq Kn \doteq p_r' \quad (3.20)$$

where, following equation 3.12,

$$K \equiv N_t/N_c \exp \frac{\lfloor E_{tn}, E_c \rfloor}{kT}$$

The density of free electrons is

$$n = f\tau_n = \frac{f}{p_r' v s_n} = \frac{f}{Knv s_n} \quad (3.21)$$

and, hence,

$$n = \left(\frac{f}{Kv s_n}\right)^{1/2} \quad (3.22)$$

In brief, the free-electron density in the transition range increases only as the square root of the light intensity, while the
free-hole density increases linearly (since n_r and therefore τ_p
are constant). In this way the densities of free electrons and
free holes approach each other and become, finally, equal when
$n + n_t > n_r$. In this way also, the occupancy of the recombination centers is modified from its initial values n_r, p_r to the values
n_r', p_r' that fit the equality of n and p.

3.6   Electronic Doping

We discuss here a most versatile concept for the understanding of the behavior of photoconductors: that of "electronic doping."

In the preceding sections, recombination centers were shown to govern the lifetime of carriers, that is, the sensitivity of photoconductors. Trapping states, on the other hand, played only an indirect role in determining the sensitivity but were responsible for response times far in excess of lifetimes. The recombination centers were located so far from the band edges that thermal excitation to the band edges could obviously be neglected in comparison with rates of kinetic capture of free electrons and holes. By contrast, the trapping states were located close enough to a band edge that thermal exchange of electrons or holes with the band edge far exceeded the rate of capture of carriers from the opposite band edge. These distinctions between trapping states and recombination centers were qualitative. An approximate quantitative distinction between trapping states and recombination centers can be made using the steady-state Fermi levels as fiduciary marks. This approximation will be justified shortly.

For the present let it be assumed that states lying between the steady-state Fermi level for electrons and the conduction band are trapping states for electrons. The steady-state Fermi level for electrons, E_{fn}, is defined as that Fermi level consistent with the density of electrons in the conduction band. Its energetic distance from the conduction band is given by

$$n = N_c \exp\left[-\frac{\lfloor E_{fn}, E_c \rfloor}{kT} \right] \tag{3.23}$$

Similarly, the energetic distance from the valence band of the steady-state Fermi level for holes, E_{fp}, is given by

$$p = N_v \exp\left[-\frac{\lfloor E_{fp}, E_v \rfloor}{kT} \right] \tag{3.24}$$

Let the states lying between the steady-state Fermi level for holes and the valence band be trapping states for holes. And let the states lying between the two steady-state Fermi levels be recombination centers. Figure 3.4 shows the location of the steady-state Fermi levels at a low and an intermediate level of excitation. In Figure 3.4a the states labeled I are recombination centers and those labeled II are traps. In Figure 3.4b, at a higher level of excitation, both states I and states II are embraced by the steady-state Fermi levels and hence both groups of states make up the complement of recombination centers.

What has happened is that an increase in the level of excitation has brought the II states into the category of recombination

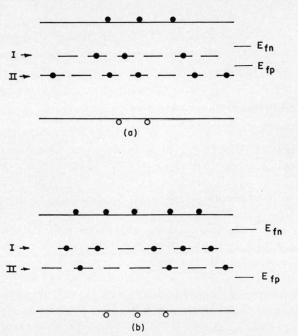

(a)

(b)

Fig. 3.4. Electronic doping (a) at a low level of excitation and (b) at an intermediate level of excitation.

centers. In brief, the photoconductor has been "doped" electronically (i.e., by increase of the level of excitation) with the II states just as effectively as if one had gone through the process of physically or chemically incorporating them in the host crystal.

"Electronic doping" is a powerful concept because the II states may be chosen *arbitrarily*. Their capture cross sections for free carriers may be chosen to sensitize or desensitize the photoconductor when they are electronically added to the group of recombination centers. Hence, one has a simple and wide-ranging mechanism to account for the dependence of photocurrent (i.e., lifetime) on light intensity.

We will make use of this concept to account for current–light curves having an odd power dependence, for the surprising phenomenon of supralinearity; and for the less surprising phenomenon of sublinearity. First, the concept of the demarcation between trapping states and recombination centers will be made more precise.

3.7 Demarcation Levels

Insulators have a more or less continuous distribution of defect states throughout the forbidden zone. Distasteful as this prospect may appear to those schooled in the practice of dealing with single, highly discrete levels, there is ample evidence to support it as a reality that must be incorporated in any complete treatment of insulators. It is true that the density of certain levels may loom large against this quasi-continuum of states and that they merit the special attention they have received to identify their physical or chemical origin. However, it is also true that photoconductivity is an incisive tool for probing a low density of background states even in the presence of high concentrations of states at a few well-defined levels. As to the origin of this quasi-continuum, the clustering of defects and the location of chemical impurities at a variety of crystalline defects may account for much of it. Evidence for the latter is that the quasi-continuum of states is more prominent, as one might expect, in evaporated and polycrystalline films than in single crystals.

Whether one grants the quasi-continuum or not, there is a sufficient scattering of states throughout the forbidden zone to justify the development of a quantitative criterion for distinguishing traps from recombination centers. What we seek at this point is an energy level at which an electron will have equal probabilities of being excited into the conduction band and of capturing a free hole. This will be the demarcation level for electrons such that states lying above this level will act predominantly as traps and those below predominantly as recombination centers. The states we are discussing here are assumed to be of one class in the sense of having a common cross section s_n for capturing a free electron and a common cross section s_p for capturing a free hole, even though these states may be distributed in energy.

The electron demarcation level D_n is defined by the following equality:

$$\nu_n{}^* \exp\left(-\frac{|D_n, E_c|}{kT}\right) = pvs_p \qquad (3.25)$$

The left-hand side of equation 3.25 is the rate of thermal excitation of an electron into the conduction band. $\nu_n{}^*$ is often regarded as the product of the highest lattice frequency and a constant less than or equal to unity, expressing the probability that an electron excited energetically to the conduction band will actually pass into the conduction band. An additional factor contained in $\nu_n{}^*$ is the ratio of states at the height of the conduction band above the ground state, (these being the number of states into which the electron can be excited) to the number of states in, or the degeneracy of, the ground state. It is worth mentioning this last factor because in principle $\nu_n{}^*$ can exceed the highest lattice frequency. On the other hand, a close examination of the component factors in $\nu_n{}^*$ is not necessary since, by an argument of detailed balance (see, e.g., Rose 1951)

$$\nu_n{}^* = N_c v s_n \qquad (3.26)$$

Equation 3.26 is used to replace $\nu_n{}^*$ in equation 3.25 and the resulting expression is solved for $\left| D_n, E_c \right|$, to get

$$\left| D_n, E_c \right| = kT \ln [N_c s_n / p s_p] \qquad (3.27)$$

We recall that formally

$$n = f / v s_n p_r$$

$$p = f / v s_p n_r$$

and

$$\frac{p}{n} = \frac{s_n p_r}{s_p n_r} \qquad (3.28)$$

Equation 3.28 is used to eliminate p from equation 3.27 with the result

$$\left| D_n, E_c \right| = kT \ln [N_c n_r / n p_r] \qquad (3.29)$$

We use the definition of the steady-state Fermi level for electrons

$$n = N_c \exp \left[-\frac{\left| E_{fn}, E_c \right|}{kT} \right]$$

to eliminate n in equation 3.29 and have finally

$$\left| D_n, E_c \right| = \left| E_{fn}, E_c \right| + kT \ln [n_r / p_r] \qquad (3.30)$$

Equation 3.30 states that to a first approximation the electron demarcation level, D_n, is located at the steady-state Fermi level, E_{fn}. In the second approximation, the demarcation level is displaced from the Fermi level by the correction term $kT \ln [n_r / p_r]$. Obviously, when $n_r \approx p_r$, the correction term is negligible. Equation 3.30 can also be written with the help of equation 3.28 in the form

$$\left| D_n, E_c \right| = \left| E_{fn}, E_c \right| + kT \ln [n s_n / p s_p] \qquad (3.31)$$

By a parallel argument, beginning with

$$v_p{}^* \exp\left[-\frac{\left| D_p, E_v \right|}{kT} \right] = nvs_p \qquad (3.32)$$

to find the demarcation level, D_p, for holes, we obtain

$$\left| D_p, E_v \right| = \left| E_{fp}, E_v \right| - kT \ln \left[n_r \, p_r \right] \qquad (3.33)$$

or

$$\left| D_p, E_v \right| = \left| E_{fp}, E_v \right| - kT \ln \left[ns_n/ps_p \right] \qquad (3.34)$$

Equations 3.33 and 3.34 state that the demarcation level for holes is to a first approximation coincident with the steady-state Fermi level for holes. In the second approximation it is displaced from it by the same amount and in the same direction (i.e., up or down) as is the electron demarcation level from its Fermi level. Another way of stating it is that when the demarcation levels are displaced from their Fermi levels, the displacement is rigid—keeping the same spacing between demarcation levels as between Fermi levels.

Equations 3.31 and 3.34 show that when there are two sets of recombination centers, each characterized by its own pair of capture cross sections s_n and s_p, the demarcation levels are displaced independently for each set from the common Fermi levels by the appropriate energies

$$kT \ln \left(ns_n/ps_p \right)$$

We need to know n/p in order to define these displacements. There is no analytic procedure, or at least no simple one, for determining n/p. On the other hand, a succession of trial values for n/p or, better, a succession of trial values of the corresponding steady-state Fermi levels can readily be tested for self consistency, since the free-carrier densities vary exponentially with displacement of the Fermi levels, while the lifetimes vary as some slow linear function of the displacement. Self consistency means fitting the relations $n = f\tau_n$ and $p = f\tau_p$ for a given f. A simplified illustration of this fitting procedure is given in Sections 3.11 and 3.12 on Sensitization and Supralinearity.

We explore now the meaning and the utility of the demarcation levels and make use of Figure 3.5. For definiteness we have chosen $n_r \gg p_r$ and have accordingly displaced the demarcation levels downward from their respective Fermi levels. We will explore the occupancy and trap-versus-recombination character of states at various energy levels. Since we have only one set of demarcation levels, we are compelled in this discussion to regard all of the states as having substantially the same cross section, s_n, for electrons and the same cross section, s_p, for holes. However, $s_n \neq s_p$.

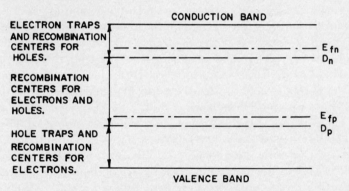

Fig. 3.5. Demarcation levels.

States lying at D_n have equal roles as traps and recombination centers, since an electron in one of these states is equally likely to be thermally excited into the conduction band and to capture a free hole. States lying above D_n rapidly take on a predominantly trap character, since the rate of thermal exchange with the conduction band increases exponentially by the Boltzmann factor at a rate of about 100 (at room temperature) for each 0.1 volt displacement above D_n. Since the probability for capturing a hole does not change with a shift in energy, a state 0.1 volt above D_n is acting 99% of the time as a trap and 1% of the time as a recombination center. In other words, for each 100 times an electron falls into such a state from the conduction band, 99 times the electron is thermally re-excited into the conduction band and only once (on the average) does it capture a free hole. For a state 0.2 volts above D_n, the ratio of its trap to recombination roles is almost 10^4 to 1. By this argument it is clear that states above D_n are in thermal contact with the conduction band and their occupancy is given by the Fermi function centered on E_{fn}.

At this point we pause to note that while E_{fn} was formally defined only in terms of the free-electron density and had no necessary connection with the occupancy of other states, we find now that E_{fn} gives the proper occupancy to a high degree of approximation of all states lying between the conduction band edge and the electron demarcation level (or within a small fraction of a volt of the demarcation level). For this reason, the steady-state Fermi levels have more physical content here than in the purely formal use of such levels in semiconductor device analyses, where they are used only for analytic convenience as a substitute for the densities of free carriers.

For states lying 0.1 volt below D_n, the rate of thermal excitation to the conduction band has already dropped to 1% of the rate of capturing free holes. Hence the kinetic process of capturing free holes is the dominant role of electron-occupied states lying between D_n and D_p. Further, electrons falling into *any* empty states between D_n and the valence band are part of the recombination traffic.

By parallel arguments, the states lying between D_p and the valence band act predominantly as hole traps and their occupancy is given by the Fermi function centered on E_{fp}. Also, the dominant role of hole-occupied states between D_p and D_n is the capture of free electrons. And holes falling into any electron-occupied states above D_p are part of the recombination traffic.

From these arguments we conclude that the occupancy of states lying between D_n and the conduction band and between D_p and the valence band is governed by their respective steady-state Fermi levels and that the character of these states is predominantly trap-like. The occupancy of states lying between

D_n and D_p is governed by the kinetic processes of capturing free electrons and free holes and this occupancy is uniform, that is, the same at all energies between D_n and D_p. Further, the states lying between D_n and D_p are predominantly recombination centers.

What is still missing in this summary is, for example, the treatment of the recombination traffic of electrons into the unoccupied states lying between D_p and the valence band. While this traffic is a legitimate part of the recombination process, its contribution to recombination can usually (but not always) be neglected, since the density of unoccupied states falls off exponentially as one departs from D_p towards the valence band.

The same argument can be made for neglecting the contribution to recombination of the free-hole traffic into the exponentially decreasing number of electron-occupied states above E_{fn}. The free-hole traffic into the states between D_n and E_{fn} is, however, not negligible, since by the choice of E_{fn} and D_n these states are almost fully occupied with electrons.

What we wish to gain out of this discussion is a procedure for counting n_r and p_r. The procedure, then, is to count all electron-occupied states above D_p as part of n_r and to add to this the electron-occupied states between D_p and the valence band weighted by the factor $\exp [- \mid D_p, E \mid /kT]$, where $\mid D_p, E \mid$ is the energy interval between these states and D_p, and where the weighting factor accounts for their exponentially decreasing role as recombination centers. For most purposes the above counting reduces to the number of electron-occupied states between E_{fn} and D_p.

To arrive at p_r we count all unoccupied states below D_n and add to this the unoccupied states lying above D_n weighted by the factor $\exp [- \mid D_n, E \mid /kT]$, where $\mid D_n, E \mid$ is the energy interval between the states and D_n. For most purposes this counting reduces to the unoccupied states between D_p and D_n plus a fraction of all the states between D_n on E_{fn}, the fraction being the same unoccupied fraction of states valid between D_n and D_p.

While the accounting procedures have been discussed in some detail, it is worth bearing in mind that when the demarcation levels lie close to their respective steady-state Fermi levels, and when the state distribution in the forbidden zone does not vary faster than the Boltzmann factor, a good approximation to the recombination centers is simply the total electron-occupied states, n_r, between the two Fermi levels and the total unoccupied states, p_r, between these two levels.

3.8   Some Significant Models

The variety of dependencies of photocurrent on light and temperature is substantially unlimited. This statement is borne out experimentally by the fact that photocurrents have been observed to increase linearly, supralinearly, and sublinearly with increasing light intensity. Similarly, photocurrents have been observed to be insensitive to temperature as well as to increase or decrease with increasing temperature. On the analytic side, the concept of "electronic doping"; easily accounts for the variety of observations. Increasing light intensity moves the steady-state Fermi levels farther apart and thereby embraces *new* states in the category of recombination centers, while increasing temperatures reverses the process. Since the *new* states may have any arbitrary character, the problem of rationalizing any particular set of observations is not difficult. For this very reason, a particular rationalization or modeling is not likely to be unique. In the face of such a complex array of possible models, we can ask two questions: First, what are the major patterns of photoconductor behavior? And second, what are the *simplest types* of models needed to account for these patterns?

The major patterns that need to be accounted for are:

 1. Lifetime $\doteq$ constant while response time $\propto$ (light intensity)$^{-1}$

2. $I_p \propto F^\alpha$, where $1/2 \leq \alpha \leq 1$ [odd power dependence on light]

3. $I_p \propto F^\alpha$, where $\alpha > 1$ or where $\alpha < 1/2$ [supralinearity and sublinearity]

4. Sensitization: The addition of recombination states to increase the lifetime of one sign of carrier.

5. Infrared quenching: The reduction of short wavelength—induced photocurrents by the addition of radiation of longer wavelength.

6. Temperature quenching: The sharp reduction of photocurrents at some critical temperature, as the temperature is increased.

The models to be explored in the following sections are the simplest types of models (so far as the writer knows) needed to account for the several phenomena listed above.

3.9   Model to Account for the Combination of $\tau =$ Constant and $\tau_0 \propto F^{-1}$

It is a common observation to find in sensitive, photoconducting insulators, such as cadmium sulfide, that the photocurrent increases linearly or nearly so with light intensity (constant lifetime) over a wide range of light intensities, while at the same time the photoconductive response time decreases, in many cases varying linearly with the inverse of the light intensity. Sensitive crystals of CdS may have, when exposed to room light, a response time and lifetime (of free carriers) of about 10^{-3} seconds. The carrier density is in the order of $10^{15}/cm^3$. At extremely low light intensities the same crystal may still have a lifetime of 10^{-3} seconds, but its response time has increased to some minutes or hours corresponding to about 10^4 seconds. Meantime, the carrier density has dropped from $10^{15}/cm^3$ to about $10^8/cm^3$.

The model shown in Figure 3.6 readily accounts for this behavior. The model shows a high concentration of states near the dark Fermi level. The high concentration is shown schemat-

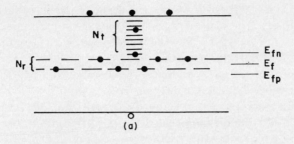

(a)

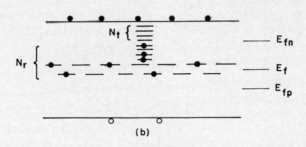

(b)

Fig. 3.6. Effect of traps on response time. (a) Low level of excitation. (b) High level of excitation.

ically by the horizontal extension of the pattern. In addition, there is a more or less uniform distribution of states of much lower density extending from the Fermi level to the conduction band. The states are shown as a single vertical column of states. The lack of horizontal extension is used to indicate schematically a low density of states. The fact that the states are shown one above the other does not mean that they are excited states of a single center. These states are actually in physically separate parts of the crystal and cannot communicate directly with each other. Electrons must pass via the conduction band, or holes via the valence band, in order to get from one state to another.

For convenience we take $n_r = p_r = 10^{16}/\text{cm}^3$ so that the

demarcation levels will be at or close to their steady-state
Fermi levels. The capture cross sections: $s_n = 10^{-20}$cm^2, $s_p = 10^{-15}$cm^2, are chosen so that the density of free electrons is large
compared with the density of free holes under photoexcitation.
The states labeled N_t can have the same capture cross sections
as those labeled N_r. Alternatively, the N_t states can have electron capture cross sections much larger than 10^{-20}cm^2. The
choice is not important. The density of N_t is 10^{11}/cm^3-kT.

Figure 3.6a shows the conditions existing under a low level
of photoexcitation [$f = 10^{10}$/cm^3-sec]. The distribution of electrons and holes in the recombination states has been homogenized. Also, some of the N_t states now appear between the two
steady-state Fermi levels and form part of the recombination
state category. Their number, however, is small enough compared with N_r to be negligible.

We can write by inspection of Figure 3.6a

$$\tau_n = \frac{1}{p_r v s_n} = \frac{1}{10^{16}10^710^{-20}} = 10^{-3} \text{ sec} \qquad (3.35)$$

$$\tau_p = \frac{1}{n_r v s_p} = \frac{1}{10^{16}10^710^{-15}} = 10^{-8} \text{ sec} \qquad (3.36)$$

$$n = f\tau_n = 10^{10}\,10^{-3} = 10^7/\text{cm}^3 \qquad (3.37)$$

$$p = f\tau_p = 10^{10}\,10^{-8} = 10^2/\text{cm}^3 \qquad (3.38)$$

$$\tau_{0n} = \left(1 + \frac{n_t}{n}\right)\tau_n = \frac{10^{11}}{10^7}\,10^{-3} = 10 \text{ sec} \qquad (3.39)$$

τ_{0p} is not significant, since the photocurrent is dominated by
free electrons.

Figure 3.6b shows the conditions existing under a high level
of photoexcitation, $f = 10^{16}$/cm^3 sec. While additional N_t states
have been brought into the category of recombination centers,
their number is still negligible, so that we can take as before:

$$\tau_n = 10^{-3} \text{ sec}$$

$$\tau_p = 10^{-8} \text{ sec}$$

and compute, further, that

$$n = 10^{13}/\text{cm}^3$$

$$p = 10^8/\text{cm}^3$$

$$\tau_{0n} = \left(1 + \frac{n_t}{n}\right)\tau_n = \left(1 + \frac{10^{11}}{10^{13}}\right)\tau_n \doteq \tau_n = 10^{-3} \text{ sec} \quad (3.40)$$

This model satisfies the conditions that the lifetime be insensitive to light intensity and the response time decrease markedly with increasing light intensity. It is clear that the N_t states need not be strictly uniformly distributed to give this result and, in fact, they need not extend throughout the upper half of the forbidden zone. Since it is only the slice of N_t states near the Fermi level that contribute to the response time, the N_t states need only be spread over a range of energies through which the steady-state Fermi level for electrons moves. In this case, the range is about 0.3 volts corresponding to a 10^6-fold range of electron density at room temperature.

From equation 3.39 it is evident that at fixed light intensity, f, the response time remains invariant as the sensitivity of the photoconductor is reduced, since $n/\tau_n = f = \text{constant}$.

Inspection of Figure 3.6b shows that while an increase of temperature will move the steady-state Fermi levels closer together, neither the lifetime nor the response time will be significantly affected. Hence, in this model, both the photocurrent and response time (at a given light intensity) are insensitive to temperature.

The model discussed here differs from that discussed in Section 3.3 only in that the N_t states are distributed in energy rather than being localized at some level between E_{fn} and the conduction band. In the model of Section 3.3, the response time did not change with light intensity. Here it does. Since there is no other model, to the writer's knowledge, for obtaining in a homogeneous photoconductor the decrease of response time with increasing light intensity while keeping the lifetime constant, this model constitutes a significant argument for a continuous distribution of localized states in the forbidden zone.

It is well to note also that the response time is an extremely sensitive probe for detecting even a trace density of trapping states. For example, under the low light conditions of Figure 3.6a, the density of N_t states need only be greater than $10^7/\text{cm}^3$-kT near the steady-state Fermi level to cause the response time to exceed the lifetime by easily measurable factors. It is perhaps for this reason that low-density background continua of states are often overlooked by other methods of observation that lack the incisiveness of the response time measurement.

3.10 Model to Account for $I_p \propto F^\alpha$; $(\frac{1}{2} \leq \alpha \leq 1)$

A common example of the variation of the photocurrent as some non-integer power of the light intensity is that of Sb_2S_3 as used in the television camera tube known as the Vidicon. Here $I_p \propto F^{0.68}$ over a wide range of light intensities.

One can find attempts to account for such an odd power in terms of a mixture of monomolecular and bimolecular processes. This is patently invalid except for a narrow range of light intensities covering a factor of order 2 over which the linear relation of a monomolecular process may give way to the square root relation of a bimolecular process. Such a mixture does not account for non-integer powers extending over several powers of ten of light intensity. Hence the need for a proper model.

The model in Figure 3.7a differs from that used in the previous section in two respects: (1) the p_r states are negligible or absent at zero light intensity, (2) the N_t states have an exponential distribution in energy such that

$$N_t(E) = A \exp\left(-\frac{|E_c, E_t|}{kT_1}\right) \tag{3.41}$$

The temperature, T_1, is a formal parameter that can be ad-

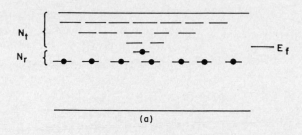

(a)

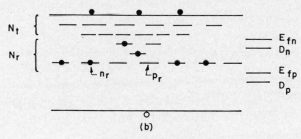

(b)

Fig. 3.7. Model for exponents of current–light curve lying between 0.5 and 1.0. (a) Unilluminated. (b) Illuminated.

justed to make the density of states vary more or less rapidly with energy. In the present discussion we take $T_1 \geq T$, where T is the ambient temperature. [The condition $T_1 < T$ reduces the problem to that already treated in Section 3.5, as will be shown below].

Let

$$N_r > \int_{Ef}^{E_c} N_t(E) \ dE$$

and, for convenience of argument, let the capture cross sections of the N_t states be the same as those for the N_r states. Actually, the capture cross sections of the N_t states may differ markedly from those of the N_r states without affecting the main argument. For definiteness, we take $s_n \ll s_p$ so that the density of photoexcited electrons is much larger than that of photoexcited holes, i.e., $n \gg p$.

Figure 3.7b shows the conditions at some intermediate light intensity. E_{fn} and E_{fp} are the steady-state Fermi levels defined by the densities n and p. The demarcation levels D_n, D_p are shifted slightly down from E_{fn} and E_{fp} because $n_r \gg p_r$. For example, if $n_r = 10^2 p_r$, the shift is about 0.1 volts at room temperature. The distribution of electrons and holes in the states lying between D_n and D_p is homogeneous and independent of energy.

There is now a simple physical picture to account for exponents less than unity derived from the distribution of N_t states. As the light intensity is increased, more and more of the N_t states are converted from trapping to recombination states. This conversion takes place as the steady-state Fermi level E_{fn} sweeps through the N_t states towards the conduction band. As p_r, the density of recombination states for electrons, increases, the electron lifetime decreases. This is what is meant by an exponent less than unity.

To a good approximation, the density of empty states p_r is given by the number of N_t states lying between the original Fermi level E_f in Figure 3.7b and the steady-state Fermi level E_{fn}. These were originally empty states that have now been brought into the category of recombination centers. A more accurate treatment would make a correction for the states lying between E_{fn} and D_n. The correction, however, would not alter p_r by more than the fraction p_r/n_r. Since we have taken this ratio to be small, the simple estimate of p_r is justified

$$
\begin{aligned}
p_r &= \int_{E_f}^{E_{fn}} N_t(E) \ dE \\
&= \int_{E_f}^{E_{fn}} A \ \exp\left[-\frac{\mid E_c, E_t \mid}{kT_1} \right] dE \qquad (3.42) \\
&\doteq kT_1 N_t(E_{fn})
\end{aligned}
$$

Hence we can write:

$$n = f\tau_n = f\left(\frac{1}{p_r v s_n}\right)$$

$$= f\frac{1}{kT_1 A \exp\left[-\frac{|E_c, E_{fn}|}{kT_1}\right] v s_n} \tag{3.43}$$

By definition,

$$n = N_c \exp\left[-\frac{|E_c, E_{fn}|}{kT}\right]$$

$$= N_c \exp\left[-\frac{|E_c, E_{fn}| T_1}{kT_1 T}\right] \tag{3.44}$$

Insertion of equation 3.44 into equation 3.43 leads to

$$n = \left[\frac{fN_c^{T/T_1}}{kT_1 A v s_n}\right]^{T_1/(T+T_1)} \tag{3.45}$$

Since $T_1 \geq T$, the exponent $T_1/(T + T_1)$ lies between 0.5 and unity.

We have in equation 3.45 a simple mechanism to account for photocurrents that increase with increasing light intensity as any power lying between 0.5 and unity. While the model assumed an exponential distribution of states lying between E_f and E_c, the distribution need only extend over the small range of energies through which E_{fn} moves, since the largest contribution to p_r comes from states near E_{fn}. Further, the distribution need only be approximated by an exponential form over this short range of energies. Hence, almost any distribution of states will lead to exponents of the current–light curve lying between 0.5 and unity. As the distribution approaches more nearly a uniform one, that is, constant in energy, the characteristic temperature $T_1 \to \infty$ and n varies more nearly linearly with light intensity.

The treatment of a strictly uniform distribution can be done more directly without use of the characteristic temperature (see, e.g., Rose, 1951). Since it introduces no novelty it will not be discussed further. If the distribution of states actually decreases toward the conduction band (negative T_1), the linear dependence of n on light intensity is only emphasized.

If the characteristic temperature $T_1 < T$, the major contribution to p_r comes from states lying between E_{fn} and E_c, namely, from shallow traps whose occupancy is related to the free-carrier density by a constant. This is just the case treated in Section 3.5 leading to an exponent 0.5 for the current versus light curve.

From this discussion we see that an exponent lying *between* 0.5 and unity (and not equal to 0.5 or unity) requires a distribution of states in energy. The writer knows of no other state distribution short of a continuous distribution of states to account for such exponents. Hence, we feel that the appearance of odd exponents between 0.5 and unity are strong evidence for a continuous distribution of states. In this argument, the mobility and capture cross sections are assumed to be constant and the photoconductor homogeneous. Bube has shown that the mobility does vary in some cases with light intensity, owing to a change of charge on the discrete states and a consequent change of scattering by charged centers. The variation in mobility must, of course, be divided out before testing the above model.

While a continuous distribution of states is needed to account for exponents between 0.5 and unity, it is not true (as is often felt) that the assumption of a continuous distribution can rationalize any observed behavior. In particular, the observation of supralinearity, i.e., exponents greater than unity, cannot be accounted for in terms of distributions of states of one class: "one class" meaning the same capture cross sections. Two classes of recombination centers, as discussed in Section 3.12, are needed.

In the present argument, it was assumed that the light excited electrons from the valence to the conduction band giving rise to free pairs. Owing to the higher density and larger capture cross section of the n_r states, the free holes were rapidly captured

into the recombination states leaving the free-electron density
of major interest. It is clear that if the light were absorbed by
the recombination (n_r) states initially, the holes would be
generated directly in the recombination centers. The result
would be closely the same as if the holes had been generated in
the valence band and rapidly captured into the recombination
centers. This type of photogeneration, in fact, makes the analysis even simpler and freer from approximation. For example, the
steady-state Fermi level for electrons approximates even more
closely the properties of a thermal equilibrium Fermi level, since
the occupancy of the trapping states is controlled only by
thermal exchange with the conduction band and is not per-
turbed by the capture traffic of free holes. Moreover, the spectral
response of photoconductors can in this way be tailored to
include photon energies less than the band gap energy if a sufficient density of recombination centers is located at the appropriate distance in energy from the conduction band.

From equation 3.43 we note that the lifetime of free electrons
is inversely proportional to the density of N_t states near the
steady-state Fermi level for electrons. At the same time, the
ratio of response time to lifetime (see equation 3.39) is proportional to this density. Hence, an increase in the density of the
N_t states would reduce the sensitivity (or lifetime) of the photoconductor while leaving the response time at fixed carrier
density invariant.

3.11 Sensitization

It is convenient to discuss the mechanism of sensitization
prior to that of supralinearity, since the latter concept follows
readily in terms of "electronic doping."

Experimentally, a relatively pure crystal of cadmium sulfide
is found to have electron and hole lifetimes in the range of 10^{-6}
to 10^{-8} sec. Such a crystal is regarded as an insensitive photoconductor. It can be converted into a sensitive photoconductor
by the addition of the localized states formed by cadmium

vacancies. The electron lifetime is then in the range of 10^{-2} to 10^{-3} sec, and the hole lifetime shorter than 10^{-8} sec. The crystal has been sensitized by the *addition* of recombination centers. The *addition* of recombination centers has *increased* the lifetime of one sign of carrier and decreased the lifetime of the other sign of carrier. The increase in lifetime by the addition of recombination centers is contrary to the intuitive expectations, namely, that more recombination centers mean shorter lifetimes.

The intuitive expectation is borne out in semiconductors in which electron and hole lifetimes are equal. There, the only means for increasing the common lifetime of free pairs is to remove recombination centers. Similarly, in photoconductors in which electron and hole lifetimes are not equal, the addition of recombination centers *of the same kind as those already present* (assuming only one kind to be present) can only decrease the lifetimes of one or both carriers and cannot increase them. The remnant possibility is that the addition of recombination centers of a *second* kind can increase the lifetime of *one* sign of carrier. This is the model for sensitization. A simple quantitative example is chosen to illustrate the model.

Figure 3.8a shows a photoconductor having one kind or class of recombination centers whose capture cross sections for both electrons and holes is 10^{-15} cm². In general, electron and hole capture cross sections will be different. For simplicity of discussion we take them to be equal, without affecting the principle of the argument.

Similarly, we take the densities of electron-occupied and hole-occupied centers to have the same value, 10^{15}/cm³. The principle of the model does not require this equality. Both electron and hole lifetimes will then have the rather "insensitive" value of

$$\tau_n = \tau_p = (vs_{n1}p_{r1})^{-1} = 10^{-7} \text{ sec} \qquad (3.46)$$

In Figure 3.8b we have added 10^{16}/cm³ impurity states all filled with electrons and having a very small capture cross section for electrons, 10^{-20} cm², and a somewhat normal cross section for holes, 10^{-15} cm². In Figure 3.8c we show the redistri-

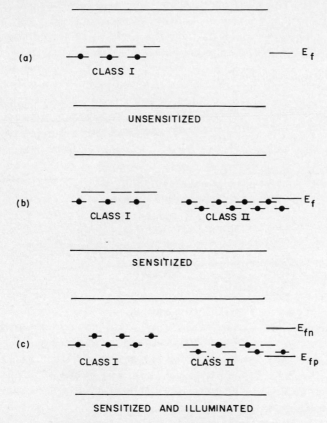

Fig. 3.8. Schematic outline of sensitization.

bution of electrons and holes that takes place among the recombination centers under illumination. Under illumination the
following steady-state condition must be rigorously satisfied.
This is the condition that the rate at which free electrons pour
into the recombination centers (individually or collectively)
must be precisely equal to the rate at which free holes pour in

$$np_{r1}vs_{n1} = pn_{r1}vs_{p1}$$
$$np_{r2}vs_{n2} = pn_{r2}vs_{p2} \qquad (3.47)$$

or

$$\frac{p_{r1}s_{n1}}{n_{r1}s_{p1}} = \frac{p_{r2}s_{n2}}{n_{r2}s_{p2}} = \frac{p}{n} \qquad (3.48)$$

In addition, the particle conservation conditions are

$$n_{r1} + p_{r1} = N_{r1} \qquad (3.49)$$

$$n_{r2} + p_{r2} = N_{r2} \qquad (3.50)$$

Equation 3.48 becomes, for $s_{n1} = s_{p1}$,

$$p_{r1} \doteq \frac{p_{r2}n_{r1}}{n_{r2}} \frac{s_{n2}}{s_{p2}} \qquad (3.51)$$

We know there will be a strong tendency to shift electrons from the N_{r2} states to the N_{r1} states, since free holes tend to accumulate in the N_{r2} states owing to the small capture cross section of these states for electrons. This shift in occupancy can only proceed to the point that

$$n_{r1} \rightarrow N_{r1}$$
$$p_{r2} \rightarrow N_{r1} \qquad (3.52)$$

and $\qquad\qquad n_{r2} \doteq N_{r2} \qquad\qquad (3.53)$

With these approximations, equation 3.51 becomes

$$p_{r1} \doteq N_{r1} \frac{N_{r1}}{N_{r2}} \frac{s_{n2}}{s_{p2}} \qquad (3.54)$$

Our assumptions that $N_{r1}/N_{r2} = 10^{-1}$ and $s_{n2}/s_{p2} = 10^{-5}$ then give

$$p_{r1} \doteq 10^{-6} N_{r1} \qquad (3.55)$$

The total rate at which electrons fall into the p_{r1} and p_{r2} states is

$$n/\tau_n = np_{r1}vs_{n1} + np_{r2}vs_{n2} \qquad (3.56)$$

from which

$$\tau_n = \frac{1}{p_{r1}vs_{n1} + p_{r2}vs_{n2}}$$

$$= \frac{1}{10^{-6}N_{r1}vs_{n1} + N_{r1}vs_{n2}} \qquad (3.57)$$

$$\doteq \frac{1}{N_{r1}vs_{n2}} = 10^{-2} \text{ sec}$$

since $10^{-6}\, s_{n1} = 10^{-1}\, s_{n2}$.

We see by comparing equations 3.57 and 3.46 that the electron lifetime has been increased from 10^{-7} to 10^{-2} sec and the photoconductor sensitized by the same factor. Meantime, the hole lifetime has been decreased from 10^{-7} to 10^{-8} sec, owing to the addition of the N_{r2} states. The sensitization has come about by a redistribution of electrons and holes between the two classes of recombination centers. In a sense, the electron recombination traffic through the N_{r1} states has been snuffed out by filling the p_{r1} states with electrons from the n_{r2} states. The holes that were in the N_{r1} states and had a large cross section for electrons have now been shifted to the N_{r2} states where their capture cross section is smaller by five powers of ten.

In the illustration chosen here, about 90% of the recombination traffic passes through the N_{r2} states, since 90% of the holes go to these states. If s_{p2} had been chosen to be 10^{-17} cm^2 instead of 10^{-15} cm^2, the photoconductor would still be sensitized by a large factor (10^4), but now only 10% of the hole recombination traffic would pass through the N_{r2} states. If the density of N_{r2} states were considerably less than that of the N_{r1} states, they would have little effect on the sensitivity since no significant transfer of electrons from N_{r2} to N_{r1} could occur.

The behavior of two classes of recombination states has a wide range of possibilities since there are eight independent parameters needed to specify the problem. We have selected a few of the more significant possibilities chiefly to illustrate the phenomenon of sensitization.

3.12 Supralinearity

It is frequently found that the photocurrent increases as some high power (e.g., 3 to 5) of the light intensity over a short range of light intensities. Before and after the transition, the photocurrent may vary approximately linearly with light intensity. Figure 3.9 shows a set of current–light curves obtained by R. H. Bube for CdS over a range of temperatures. The logarithmic shift of the sharp transition along the light intensity axis is approximately proportional to (absolute temperature)$^{-1}$. The increase of photocurrent as a high power of the light intensity is called supralinearity.

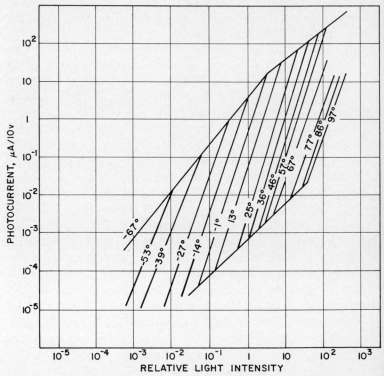

Fig. 3.9. Data on supralinearity in CdS (R. H. Bube).

Supralinearity is a particularly striking effect since most of the changes that one would expect to occur at higher light intensities lead to sublinearity. Moreover, the supralinearity that is experimentally observed can occur at a relatively low light level where saturation of recombination centers is not likely to take place. Even so, most saturation effects also lead to sublinearity. In brief, the problem of accounting for supralinearity is not the usual one of choosing between a number of equally reasonable models but of finding even one model.

The model for supralinearity shown in Figure 3.10 follows easily from the two concepts: sensitization (Section 3.11) and "electronic doping" (Section 3.6). In Figure 3.10a we show a photoconductor under low illumination such that the two

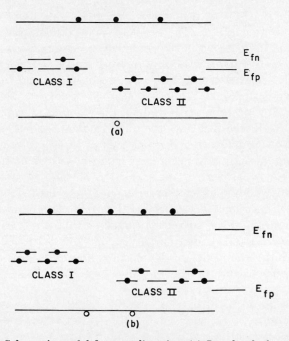

Fig. 3.10. Schematic model for supralinearity. (a) Low level of excitation. (b) Intermediate level of excitation.

steady-state Fermi levels embrace a set of recombination centers called class I states. These states have about equal capture cross sections for electrons and holes; e.g., 10^{-15} cm^2. If the density of these states is 10^{15}/cm^3, the electron and hole lifetimes will be about 10^{-7} sec, as in the previous section. A second set of levels, class II states, is located below and outside the two steady-state Fermi levels sufficiently removed to qualify as hole traps rather than as recombination centers. For the class II states the capture cross section for electrons is 10^{-20} cm^2 and for holes 10^{-15} cm^2. The density of the class II states is well in excess of the class I states.

Figure 3.10b shows that at some higher light intensity the steady-state Fermi levels have moved apart sufficiently to embrace the class II states as well as the class I states, so that there are now two sets of recombination centers just as in the preceding section (3.11). The result of incorporating the class II states in the category of recombination centers is to sensitize the photoconductor, that is, to increase the electron lifetime by some five powers of ten. This is an example of sensitization by "electronic doping." While the class II states are being converted into recombination centers, the electron lifetime is continuously increasing and the photocurrent increases supralinearly with increasing light intensity. After full conversion, the photocurrent again increases linearly with light intensity.

A strict treatment of the transition of class II states from traps to recombination centers should take into account the demarcation levels, a separate set for each class of states. The problem is, however, sufficiently involved that it is questionable how much detailed information can be deduced from a given set of data. The utility of the model is mainly to give a simple qualitative picture of the way in which supralinearity comes about.

The shift of the supralinear section of Bube's curves along the light intensity axis as the temperature is increased fits easily into the model. Since the steady-state Fermi level E_{fp} is defined by the relation

$$| E_{fp}, E_v | = -kT \ln (p/N_v) \qquad (3.58)$$

one expects that at fixed light intensity (fixed p) it would recede from the band edge at a rate proportional to the absolute temperature. Hence, as the temperature is increased, a higher light intensity is required to cause the steady-state Fermi levels to embrace the class II states and initiate the supralinear behavior.

Quantitatively, we can expect, if p is proportional to light intensity f, that at the onset of supralinearity:

$$\frac{\Delta f}{f} = \frac{| E_{fp}, E_v |}{kT} \frac{\Delta T}{T} \qquad (3.59)$$

Equation 3.59 is obtained from equation 3.58 by differentiation and replacing differentials by finite differences. It gives the fractional change in light intensity required to balance a fractional change in temperature in order to remain at the onset of supralinearity.

3.13 Infrared and Thermal Quenching

A frequent observation is that a given photocurrent excited by light in the visible part of the spectrum can be considerably reduced or "quenched" by the addition of infrared light. This is particularly true for the more sensitive photoconductors, CdS again being a prominent example.

The model for this effect (Fig. 3.11) is the same as the model for supralinearity discussed in Section 3.12. Suppose that a supralinear photoconductor has been illuminated so that it has passed the supralinear transition and is now in the sensitive state. This means that the sensitizing class II states have been converted from traps to recombination centers. As noted at the end of the last section, an increase in temperature at fixed light intensity will cause the photoconductor to revert to the insensitive state by shifting the steady-state Fermi levels farther from the band edges so that the sensitizing states become traps instead of recombination centers. This phenomenon is known as temperature quenching.

In place of heating the entire photoconductor, one can think of "heating" the sensitizing centers (class II states) selectively. This is accomplished by using infrared light that is selectively absorbed by the class II states. Electrons are thereby excited

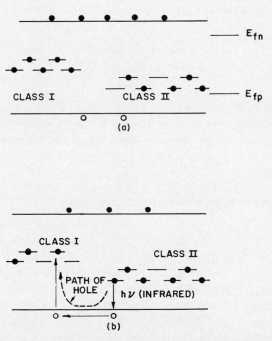

Fig. 3.11. Model for infrared quenching. (a) Supralinear photoconductor illuminated with strongly absorbed light. (b) Addition of infrared light to Figure 3.11a.

from the valence band into the class II states and the resultant free holes are captured by the class I (or insensitive) states. Since the process of sensitization had shifted holes from class I to class II states, this is the reverse process or one of desensitization. The infrared may be regarded as coupling the class II states closer to the valence band just as would occur with an increase in lattice temperature.

The work of Bube is consistent with this model of infrared quenching and was used by Bube to define the energy interval between the class II states and the valence band. These data were also consistent with the same energy deduced by Bube from thermal quenching.

Semiconductors

The discussions of recombination in the preceding sections were concerned with insulators in which the thermally generated free-carrier density was small compared with the optically generated densities. For the most part, also, the densities of optically generated carriers were small compared with the densities of recombination centers. The latter condition led to independent lifetimes for electrons and holes. We consider now the semiconductor type of recombination in which the optically created densities are perturbations on the thermal densities.

A particular class of these problems has the additional feature that the lifetimes of electrons and holes are necessarily equal. These lifetimes are the times required for the optically per-turbed densities to relax to their thermal equilibrium values. While the general conditions for the equality of lifetimes will be discussed in Section 3.15, a sufficient condition is that the densities of optically generated electrons and holes both be large compared with the densities of recombination centers. In this case, it is clear that, by the condition of charge neutrality, the difference between electron and hole densities, which dif-ference must appear in the recombination states, must be small compared with the densities of either electrons or holes. Since the electron and hole densities are nearly equal, so also must be their lifetimes. We discuss first this special case of equality of lifetimes because it is readily resolved in terms of the concepts of demarcation levels and because it is the all-important condi-tion for bipolar transistors.

3.14   Semiconductors: Equal Electron and Hole Lifetimes

Since, by assumption, the lifetimes of electrons and holes are equal, we can choose to analyze the simpler of the two, namely, that of the minority carrier. 'Minority' here refers to the smaller density of thermal carriers. To carry out the analysis, we again define the demarcation levels for electrons and holes. We expect that both demarcation levels will coalesce into one level, since by our assumption of small perturbations on the thermal densities there is only one Fermi level—the "dark" or thermal equilibrium one.*

The demarcation level for an electron is defined as that energy level at which an electron in a localized state will have equal probabilities of being thermally excited to the conduction band and of capturing a free hole. The condition is

$$v_n{}^* \exp\left[-\frac{\mid D_n, E_c \mid}{kT} \right] = p_0 v s_p \qquad (3.60)$$

Here, p_0 is the thermal density of holes. We solve equation 3.60 for $\mid D_n, E_c \mid$ to get

$$\mid D_n, E_c \mid = kT \ln \frac{v_n{}^*}{p_0 v s_p} = kT \ln\left(\frac{v_n{}^* s_n}{p_0 v s_n s_p} \right) \qquad (3.61)$$

From detailed balance,

$$v_n{}^*/v s_n = N_c \qquad (3.62)$$

To a good approximation we can take $N_c = N_v$, since their ratio enters in only logarithmically. With this approximation equation 3.62 becomes

$$\mid D_n, E_c \mid = kT \left[\ln \frac{N_v}{p_0} + \ln \frac{s_n}{s_p} \right]$$

$$= \mid E_f, E_v \mid + kT \ln \frac{s_n}{s_p} \qquad (3.63)$$

---

* The degenerate form of demarcation levels has been used independently by Shockley [*Proc. IRE*, **46**, 973 (1958)] and dubbed the "equality level."

For $s_n = s_p$, equation 3.63 states that D_n is as far from the conduction band as E_f is from the valence band. In brief, D_n is
the mirror image of E_f reflected about the middle of the forbidden zone. The correction term to this simple mirror concept
is $kT \ln (s_n/s_p)$.

The same type of argument for D_p locates it at the same
energy level as D_n. Hence, we have only one level to deal with
which we label D as shown in Figure 3.12. The meaning of D
for electrons and holes is shown schematically on this figure.
The interval E_f–D can perhaps best be understood by referring
back to Figure 3.5 and its attendant discussion. There the states
lying in the interval E_{fn}–D_n added a correction term on the

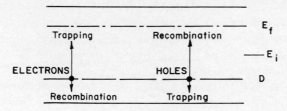

Fig. 3.12. Demarcation level for semiconductor and dominant functions
of states at various energy levels.

main body of recombination states for holes, the main body
being located between D_n and D_p. Here the interval D_n–D_p has
vanished, leaving the states between E_f and D to constitute the
main body of recombination states for holes. We use the phrase
"recombination states for holes" even though the concept of
recombination means that an identical recombination traffic of
electrons must pour into these states. In a sense the hole
traffic controls where the electron traffic will go. By the
definition of D, these states are clearly recombination states
for holes. While they are by the same definition acting predominantly as traps for electrons, a small part of the electron
traffic "leaks off" as recombination traffic—enough to match
the hole recombination traffic.

We choose, for simplicity, to examine the lifetime of an optically generated free hole. Any electron-occupied states lying above D are recombination states for such holes. This means that states between D and E_f are counted in full since they are substantially fully occupied by electrons. Those states lying between E_f and E_c become rapidly ineffective for recombination, because their occupancy by electrons approaches zero exponentially as one departs from E_f. At the same time, the states between D and E_v become rapidly ineffective as recombination centers as one departs downward from D since, by definition of D, these states act predominantly as hole traps. The weighting factor for states above E_f as well as for those below D is

$$\exp\left(-\Delta E/kT\right)$$

where ΔE is the energy interval between the states in question and E_f or D, whichever is closer. The net result is that states lying between E_f and D are counted in full as recombination centers for holes, while states lying outside these levels are weighted rapidly toward zero by the Boltzmann factor cited above.

We are in a position now to make a quick and simple analysis of the lifetime of free carriers as a function of location of the Fermi level. The location of the Fermi level is varied by varying the relative numbers of arbitrarily shallow donors and acceptors. In this way the donors and acceptors retain only their "doping" function and play a negligible role in the recombination process. To emphasize the main points of the analysis we take $s_n = s_p$ so that D is a true reflection of E_f about the middle of the forbidden zone. The more general case of $s_n \neq s_p$ is treated by the present method of analysis by Rose (1957).

Figure 3.13 shows a single level of recombination states located above the middle of the forbidden gap at the level E_r. We begin with the Fermi level near the conduction band (Fig. 3.13a) and note at the outset that the minority carrier lifetime is

$$\tau_p \equiv \frac{\Delta p}{f} = \frac{1}{N_r v s_p}$$

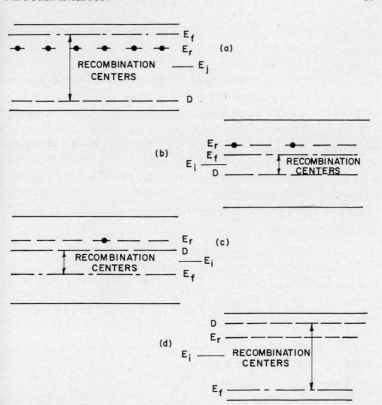

Fig. 3.13. Domain of major recombination centers as a function of Fermi level.

since the N_r states are embraced by E_f and its reflection D. This condition is maintained as the Fermi level moves from the conduction band to the level E_r. When the Fermi level moves from E_r to the middle of the forbidden band (Fig. 3.13b) its reflection D moves to the middle and meets it there. During this excursion the N_r states lie increasingly outside the interval E_f–D, and accordingly their contribution to recombination decreases exponentially as

$$\exp\left(-\Delta E/kT\right)$$

where ΔE is the energy $|\, E_r,\, E_f\,|$. Hence the lifetime increases as exp $(\Delta E/kT)$ as shown in Figure 3.14.

At the middle of the forbidden band, E_f and D cross, the latter moving towards E_r and the conduction band as E_f moves toward the valence band (Fig. 3.13c). The minority carrier has meantime switched from holes to electrons. Since the interval $|\, D,\, E_r\,|$ is decreasing, the contribution of the N_r states to recombination is now increasing at the rate exp $(-\,|\, D,\, E_r\,|/kT)$ and the minority carrier lifetime decreasing as exp $(|\, D,\, E_r\,|/kT)$ (see Fig. 3.14). When D passes through the level E_r, that is, when E_f is as far below the middle of the gap as E_r is above it (Fig. 3.13d), the lifetime levels off to the same value it had at the outset, namely,

$$\tau_n = 1/N_r v s_n$$

This illustration was chosen to emphasize the symmetry

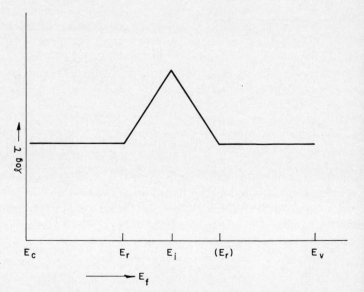

Fig. 3.14. Lifetime of free pairs as a function of Fermi level. (E_r) is the reflection of E_r about E_i.

properties of the problem via E_f and its reflection D. If the capture cross sections s_n and s_p were chosen unequal, the terminal lifetimes τ_n and τ_p would, of course, be unequal. At the same time, E_f and D would no longer cross at the middle of the forbidden gap but at a level $\frac{1}{2}kT \ln (s_n/s_p)$ removed from it.

While the above analysis was carried out for densities of optically generated carriers small compared with the thermal density of minority carriers, it remains valid in many cases even for optical densities large compared with the thermal density of minority carriers but yet small compared with the majority carrier density. Reference to Figure 3.15b shows that when the optical density of minority carriers is, for example, one hundred times the thermal density, the interval D_n-D_p will only be 1/10 volt at room temperature and may often be ignored.

One of the major advantages of the schematized analysis of Figure 3.13 is that the effects of introducing more than one level of recombination centers can easily be visualized. In general, as other recombination levels are introduced, the strong exponential dependence of lifetime on the location of the Fermi level is weakened from an exponential towards a linear dependence on energy. The latter would occur for a more or less uniform energy distribution of recombination states.

In passing, it is worth noting the exponential temperature dependence of the lifetime when the recombination states N_r lie outside the interval E_f-D. This temperature dependence has been used to locate the energy level E_r.

3.15 Semiconductor: Unequal Electron and Hole Lifetimes

The analysis carried out in Section 3.14 for the minority carrier lifetime is valid also for the present case in which the electron and hole lifetimes are not equal. The lifetime of the majority carrier is now not equal to that of the minority carrier and must be computed separately.

Perhaps the most general remark that can be made about the majority carrier lifetime is that there is no simple general formalism for arriving at it, comparable with that applied to the previous recombination problems that have been discussed. The inherent complexity of the problem is indicated by the following general relation for the ratio of electron to hole lifetimes derived from a perturbation argument (Rose, 1957):

$$\tau_n/\tau_p = \frac{(n_0 + n_1)s_n + (n_r + p_0 + p_1)s_p}{(n_0 + n_1 + p_r)s_n + (p_0 + p_1)s_p} \qquad (3.64)$$

Here n_1 and p_1 are the free electron and hole densities that would exist if the Fermi level were located at the level of recombination centers. We note that there are eight independent parameters to be specified. For most problems equation 3.64 can be simplified. For example, if we are dealing with an n-type semiconductor and the recombination state lies above the middle of the forbidden gap, we can frequently neglect the terms in p_0 and p_1 compared with n_0 and n_1. Equation 3.64 then becomes

$$\tau_n/\tau_p = \frac{(n_0 + n_1)s_n + n_r s_p}{(n_0 + n_1)s_n + p_r s_n} \qquad (3.65)$$

The condition for equality of lifetimes from equation 3.65 is that $n_0 s_n$ or $n_1 s_n$ be greater than both $n_r s_p$ and $p_r s_n$. This is the condition for equality of lifetimes for the perturbation problem of vanishingly small densities of optical carriers. The simpler condition for equality of lifetimes, namely, that the optically generated densities be greater than the recombination state densities still holds for large, optically generated densities.

For sufficiently large n_r and p_r, equation 3.65 reduces to the familiar form

$$\tau_n/\tau_p = n_r s_p/p_r s_n \qquad (3.66)$$

from which

$$\tau_n = 1/p_r v s_n$$

and

$$\tau_p = 1/n_r v s_p \tag{3.67}$$

It may also happen that

$$n_r s_p > n_0 s_n > p_r s_n \tag{3.68}$$

In this case, assuming the Fermi level to be above the recombination state level,

$$\tau_n/\tau_p = n_r s_p/n_0 s_n \tag{3.69}$$

from which

$$\tau_n = 1/n_0 v s_n$$

and

$$\tau_p = 1/n_r v s_p \tag{3.70}$$

The reason for choosing these two extremes is to show from equations 3.67 and 3.70 that the electron (majority carrier) lifetime can depend either on the recombination state density or on the free-carrier density. The above considerations apply to the problem of vanishingly small, optically generated carrier densities. For higher densities of optical carriers, it is likely that the densities of optically generated holes in the recombination states will be nearly equal to the optical density of free electrons and will exceed the thermal density of holes in the recombination states. In this case it is clear that

$$\tau_n = 1/n_0 v s_n \tag{3.71}$$

A particularly interesting case arises when there are two sets of recombination centers such that their capture cross sections for holes are comparable, while their capture cross sections for electrons are widely different. To be definite, let

$$N_{r1} = 10^{15}/\text{cm}^3, \qquad s_{n1} = 10^{-20} \text{ cm}^2, \qquad s_{p1} = 10^{-15} \text{ cm}^2$$

$$N_{r2} = 10^{17}/\text{cm}^3, \qquad s_{n2} = 10^{-15} \text{ cm}^2, \qquad s_{p2} = 10^{-15} \text{ cm}^2$$

Only one per cent of the recombination traffic of holes goes to the N_{r1} states, owing to their lower density. Yet this small traffic of holes supports 99.9% of the optically generated electron density since the N_{r1} states have a very small capture cross section for electrons. The result is as if the photocurrent were generated by only 1% of the incident light. The photocurrent will be correspondingly more noisy than if all of the light had contributed equally to it. The increased "noisiness" is formally the same as that encountered when two photomultipliers are connected in parallel. Let one photomultiplier collect only one per cent of the total light falling on both of them. If the gain is sufficiently high, the noise from this multiplier will be the dominant noise in the combined output current. The resultant ratio of average current to noise current will then be less than that for one multiplier alone—the multiplier collecting 99% of the light.

3.16   Transition from "Semiconductor" to "Insulator"

We sketch here the changes in occupancy of the discrete states in the forbidden zone that occur as the photoexcited carrier densities become large compared with the thermal densities. Since the semiconductor problem is defined by the condition that photodensities be less than thermal densities and the insulator problem by the converse, we have no choice but to increase the photoconductivity in going from "semiconductor" to "insulator." While this appears like a contradiction in terms, it will be recognized that this transition is the equivalent of decreasing the thermal densities, keeping the optical densities constant.

Figure 3.15a is a repeat of Figure 3.14, showing the single demarcation level as an approximate reflection of the Fermi level about the middle of the forbidden gap. For both optical densities less than both thermal densities, the occupancy of states is that of thermal equilibrium and is determined by the "dark" Fermi level. For minority carriers, all electron-occupied states above D are recombination centers and the bulk of these lie between D and E_f.

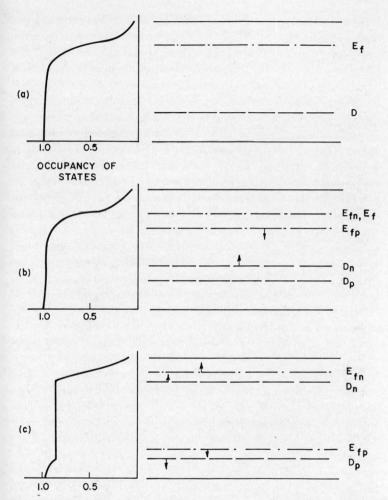

Fig. 3.15. Transition from "semiconductor" to "insulator" condition.

In Figure 3.15b, the optical density of holes exceeds the thermal density of holes, while the converse is true for electrons. This is a transition state. The Fermi level for holes, E_{fp}, now separates out from E_{fn}, which remains at the same level as E_f.

E_{fp} moves toward the valence band. At the same time D_n separates out and moves toward the conduction band at the same rate as E_{fp} moves towards the valence band. D_p remains at the same level as D. In this way, the intervals $| E_{fn}, D_n |$ and $| E_{fp}, D_p |$ are maintained equal. In the interval $| D_n, D_p |$ the occupancy of states is kinetically determined by recombination processes and is homogenized, that is, independent of energy. The occupancy of states above D_n is determined by E_{fn} and the occupancy of states below D_p is determined by E_{fp}. The states in the interval $| D_n, D_p |$ are counted in full as recombination centers for both electrons and holes depending, of course, on whether they are occupied by holes or electrons. The electron-occupied states above D_n are recombination centers for holes. Steady state requires that the recombination traffic of electrons into states above D_n be identical with the recombination traffic of holes into these states. Similarly for the states below D_p. Finally, it must be borne in mind that each set of recombination states has its own set of demarcation levels. Since the sets of demarcation levels are shifted relative to each other by an amount kT times the logarithm of the ratio of various capture cross sections, the magnitude of the shift may often be negligible.

In Figure 3.15c the transition has been completed, since both optical densities are larger than both thermal densities. The demarcation levels D_n, D_p are now well separated and are likely to embrace the major concentrations of recombination centers. E_{fn} and E_{fp}, as before, determine the occupancy of states lying outside the interval $| D_n, D_p |$. From the point of view of occupancy (Fig. 3.15c) one can see that the optical excitation can be regarded as having "shrunk" the forbidden gap by an amount $| D_n, D_p |$.

3.17 Negative Photoconductivity

The early literature on photoconductivity contains a number of observations of the reduction of current through a material

by the action of light. In the absence of a clear understanding
of photoconductivity or the complex recombination processes,
the negative photoeffect was often attributed to photochemical
effects. It is possible that some of these observations did have a
chemical origin, although, insofar as they were reversible, an
electronic origin is more likely. Well-defined observations on
the negative photoeffect in germanium have been reported more
recently by Stöckmann.

The negative photoeffect is a particularly interesting phenomenon because intuitively one expects that an excitation
process that begins with exciting free carriers can only increase
the free-carrier density. It is true that the infrared quenching
discussed in Section 3.13 is an example of adding light to reduce
conductivity. But in the case of infrared quenching one at least
has the additional degree of freedom that the conductivity
quenched by the infrared is not a thermal equilibrium conductivity. It is a conductivity induced by light of shorter wavelength. And the effect of one wavelength can conceivably be
"undone" by another wavelength. In the case of the negative
photoeffect one has to think of "undoing" a thermal equilibrium
process and this is much less obvious. As one might expect, the
conditions for its occurrence are highly specialized.

The model proposed by Stöckmann is shown in Figure 3.16.

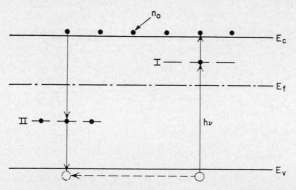

Fig. 3.16. Model for negative photoconductivity proposed by F. Stöckmann.

Qualitatively, the argument is that light excites electrons from the valence band into localized states (I) between the Fermi level and the conduction band. To emphasize the argument by exaggeration, let the rate of thermal exchange between these states and the conduction band be so small that the additional electron population causes a negligible increase in the rate of thermal generation into the conduction band. Meantime the free holes are rapidly captured by another set of states (II) lying below the Fermi level. These states have capture cross sections for electrons and holes in the neighborhood of atomic dimensions, that is, 10^{-15} cm^2 as opposed to the vanishingly small capture cross sections of the I states for electrons. The addition of holes in the II states acts as a sink for the thermal density n_0 of free electrons and causes a reduction in n_0. Hence, the thermal equilibrium density of electrons has been reduced by the action of light. Meantime, the density of free holes has been increased but not sufficiently to offset the decrease in density of free electrons. In this sense the negative photoeffect is similar to that of infrared quenching, namely, an increase in density of minority carriers followed by a larger decrease in density of majority carriers. In this sense also, intuition is partially satisfied in that the radiation at least increases the density of one sign of carrier.

A quantitative insight into the conditions for getting a negative photoeffect may be obtained by letting one photon be absorbed so that an electron is added to the I states and a hole to the II states. We assume that the free hole has been captured by the II states rapidly enough to neglect its contribution to the densty of free holes. At this point the additional electron in the I states will be thermally evaporated into the conduction band at the rate

$$\nu^* \exp\left[-\frac{\mid E_c, E_I \mid}{kT} \right] = N_c v s_{nI} \exp\left[-\frac{\mid E_c, E_I \mid}{kT} \right] \quad (3.72)$$

and the additional hole in the II states will capture an electron from the conduction band at the rate

$$n_0 v s_{nII} = N_c v s_{nII} \exp\left[-\frac{|E_c, E_f|}{kT} \right] \qquad (3.73)$$

If we are to have a negative photoeffect, we ask that

$$N_c v s_{nII} \exp\left[-\frac{|E_c, E_f|}{kT} \right] > N_c v s_{nI} \exp\left[-\frac{|E_c, E_I|}{kT} \right]$$

or

$$\frac{s_{nII}}{s_{nI}} > \exp\left[\frac{|E_I, E_f|}{kT} \right] \qquad (3.74)$$

This is an unlikely but obviously not an impossible condition. It is unlikely because states above the Fermi level tend to be electrostatically more positive than those lying below the Fermi level and, hence, to have a higher capture cross section for free electrons.

References

Broser, I., and R. Warminsky, *Ann. Physik*, 16, 361 (1955).

Bube, R. H., in R. G. Breckenridge, B. R. Russell, and E. E. Hahn, eds., *Photoconductivity Conference*, Wiley, New York–London, 1954, p. 575.

Bube, R. H., *J. Phys. Chem. Solids*, 1, 234 (1956).

Bube, R. H., *Photoconductivity*, Pergamon Press, London, 1962, p. 173 Edited by H. Levinstein.

Bube, R. H., *Solid State Physics*, Vol. II, Academic Press, New York, 1962. Edited by F. Seitz and D. Turnbull.

DeVore, H. B., *RCA Rev.*, 20, 79 (1959).

Forgue, S. V., R. R. Goodrich, and A. D. Cope, *RCA Rev.*, 12, 335 (1951).

Klasens, H. A., *J. Phys. Chem. Solids*, 7, 175 (1958).

Many, A., and R. Bray, *Progress in Semiconductors*, Vol. III, Heywood & Co., London, 1958. Edited by A. F. Gibson, P. Aigrain and R. E. Burgess.

Niekisch, E. A., *Ann. Physik*, 15, 279 (1955).

Niekisch, E. A., *Z. Phys. Chem.*, 217, 110 (1961).

Rose, A., *RCA Rev.*, 12, 362 (1951).

Rose, A., in R. G. Breckenridge, B. R. Russell, and E. E. Hahn, eds., *Photoconductivity* Conference, Wiley, New York–London, 1954, p. 3.

Rose, A., *Phys. Rev.*, 97, 322 (1955).

Rose, A., *Progress on Semiconductors*, Heywood & Co., London, Vol. II, 1957, p. 111. Edited by A. F. Gibson, P. Aigrain and R. E. Burgess.

Schön, M., *Tech. Wiss. Abh. Osram*, 6, 49 (1953).

Shockley, W., and W. T. Read, *Phys. Rev.*, 87, 835 (1952).

Smith, R. W., *RCA Rev.*, 12, 350 (1951).

Stöckmann, F., *Z. Physik*, 143, 348 (1955).

Weimer, P. K., and A. D. Cope, *RCA Rev.*, 12, 314 (1951).

Chapter 4

Space-Charge-Limited Current Flow

Throughout Chapter 3 we were content to compute the density of carriers generated by light with the understanding that the photocurrents are immediately derivable from the elementary concepts of conductivity and Ohm's law. The understanding is, of course, borne out by most normal measurements. At sufficiently high voltages, to be defined quantitatively in Chapter 5, the currents are no longer Ohmic and no longer determined by the carrier densities that were present in the absence of an applied voltage. The currents at these higher voltages are space-charge-limited currents arising from a space charge of excess carriers injected from one of the electrodes. In the present section, we neglect the thermal and photo carriers present in the absence of an applied voltage and ask only what is the behavior of space charge-limited currents in a substantial insulator. The interaction between space-charge-limited and Ohmic currents will be treated in Chapter 5. While the discussion here is in terms of electron flow, the arguments are equally valid for hole flow.

4.1 Trap-Free and Shallow-Trap Problems

The simplest insulator is, of course, a vacuum. We will derive the well-known Child-Langmuir relation for space charge-limited currents in a vacuum in order to illustrate the method of analysis to be used for solid insulators.

Figure 4.1 shows a voltage applied to a vacuum diode having

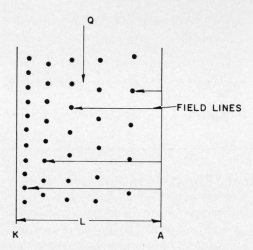

Fig. 4.1. Space-charge-limited current in vacuum.

a hot cathode. The hot cathode is assumed to supply a reservoir of free carriers in the vacuum space just outside the cathode. The applied field draws a part of this reservoir into the space between cathode and anode. All of the field lines end on charges in space. Hence, the field at the cathode (for zero emission velocity) is zero. If the charge were uniformly distributed between cathode and anode, the effective capacitance between this charge and the anode would be twice the geometric capacitance for the two plates considered as a simple condenser. We recognize that, for current continuity, the space charge is predominantly near the cathode where the electron velocity is low. Hence, to an approximation better than a factor of 2 we can say that the charge in space is given by

$$Q \doteq CV = \frac{10^{-12} \, V}{4\pi L} \text{ coulomb/cm}^2 \qquad (4.1)$$

where C is the geometric capacitance and V the applied voltage.

$$I = \frac{Q}{T_r} = \frac{V}{4\pi L^2 / \bar{v}} 10^{-12} \text{ amp/cm}^2 \qquad (4.2)$$

where T_r is the transit time of an electron from cathode to anode and $\bar{v}$ some mean velocity taken here to be half the final velocity. Thus,

$$\bar{v} = \tfrac{1}{2}\left(2\,\frac{eV}{m}\right)^{1/2} = 3 \times 10^7 V^{1/2} \text{ cm/sec} \qquad (4.3)$$

where V is in practical volts.

Insertion of equations 4.3 into equation 4.2 yields the well-known relation

$$I = \frac{3}{4\pi}\,\frac{V^{3/2}}{L^2}\,10^{-5} = 2.4\,\frac{V^{3/2}}{L^2}\,10^{-6}\,\text{amp/cm}^2 \qquad (4.4)$$

The accurate value for the constant is 2.3 rather than 2.4.

Figure 4.2 shows the solid-state analog of the vacuum diode. A low work function cathode is assumed to supply a reservoir of electrons in the conduction band of the insulator immediately

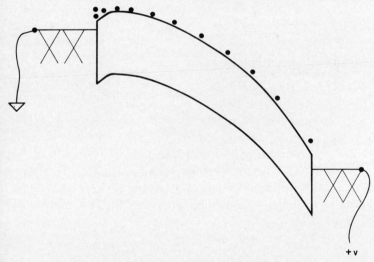

Fig. 4.2. Space-charge-limited current in a solid.

outside the cathode. This reservoir is drawn in part into the space between cathode and anode by the applied field. We approximate the charge, as before, by

$$Q = CV = \frac{KV}{4\pi L} \times 10^{-12} \text{ coulombs/cm}^2 \qquad (4.5)$$

and the transit time by

$$T_r = L^2/V\mu \qquad (4.6)$$

to obtain

$$I = \frac{Q}{T_r} = \frac{KV^2\mu}{4\pi L^3} \times 10^{-12} \text{ amp/cm}^2 \qquad (4.7)$$

The space charge-limited current is considerably smaller than that in vacuum for the same spacing and voltage because the electron velocity in the solid is much smaller than in vacuum.

In equation 4.7, the mobility, μ, is clearly the drift mobility of free carriers. If there are shallow traps present such that the ratio of free to trapped electrons is a small number:

$$\theta = \frac{n}{n_t} \ll 1 \qquad (4.8)$$

we can write equation 4.7 in the form

$$I = \frac{KV^2\theta\mu}{4\pi L^3} \times 10^{-12} \text{ amp/cm}^2 \qquad (4.9)$$

4.2 Deep Traps

We wish now to explore the more likely situation where there is a quasi-continuum of trapping states between the "dark" Fermi level and the conduction band. Let the trap distribution be given (Fig. 4.3) by

$$N_t(E) = A \exp \left[- \mid E_t, E_c \mid /kT_c\right]/\text{cm}^3\text{-ev} \qquad (4.10)$$

The parameter T_c is a characteristic temperature used to ap-

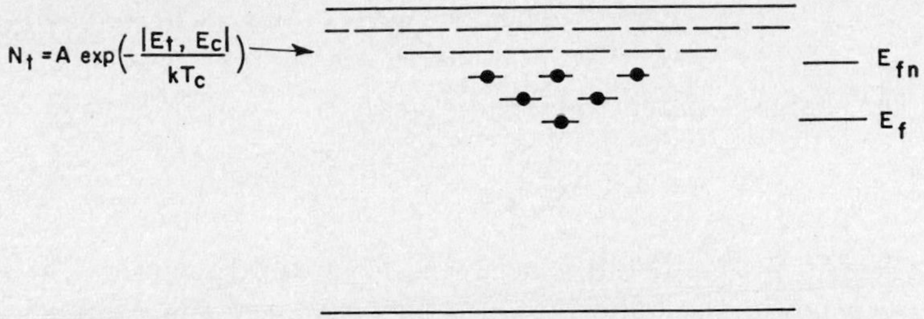

$N_t = A \exp\left(-\dfrac{|E_t,\, E_c|}{kT_c}\right) \longrightarrow$

E_{fn}

E_f

Fig. 4.3. Exponential distribution of traps.

proximate the rate at which the trap density changes with energy. $T_c \to \infty$ means a uniform distribution in energy. For T_c less than the ambient temperature T, the problem reduces to that of shallow traps given by equation 4.9. Hence, we take $T_c \geq T$. Also we assume that the density of traps is considerably larger than the density of free carriers, that is,

$$kTN_t(E) \gg N_o \exp\left(-\frac{|E_{fn},\, E_c|}{kT}\right) \qquad (4.11)$$

If the converse is true, we can, of course, neglect the traps.

A first approximation to the solution for the space-charge-limited current in the presence of a continuum of traps is obtained by assuming that the injected charge is uniformly distributed between cathode and anode. Since, also, the trap density is large compared with the free-carrier density, the injected charge will to a high degree of approximation lie in the trapping states. Hence, we can think of the Fermi level as having been raised from its initial value to E_{fn} by filling the trapping states with the injected charge. The new density of free carriers will be

$$n = N_c \exp\left(-\frac{|E_{fn},\, E_c|}{kT}\right) \qquad (4.12)$$

Since we have chosen an exponential form for the distribution of trapping states, the number of states in the interval $|E_f,\, E_{fn}| \gg kT_c$ is (see eq. 4.10):

$$kT_cN_t(E_{fn}) = kT_cA \exp\left[-\frac{|E_{fn}, E_c|}{kT_c} \right] \qquad (4.13)$$

The charge required to fill these states is

$$eLkT_cA \exp\left[-\frac{|E_{fn}, E_c|}{kT_c} \right] = VC \qquad (4.14)$$

where L is the distance between electrodes. Equation 4.14 is rewritten in the following form for convenience in computing the free-carrier density.

$$\left[\exp\left(-\frac{|E_{fn}, E_c|}{kT} \right) \right]^{T/T_c} = \frac{VC}{eLkT_cA}$$

or

$$\exp\left(-\frac{|E_{fn}, E_c|}{kT} \right) = \left(\frac{VC}{eLkT_cA} \right)^{T_c/T} \qquad (4.15)$$

Insertion of equation 4.15 in equation 4.12 gives the free-carrier density in the desired form:

$$n = BV^{T_c/T} \qquad (4.16)$$

where

$$B = N_c \left(\frac{C}{eLkT_cA} \right)^{T_c/T} = N_c \left(\frac{K\,10^{-12}}{4\pi eL^2kT_cA} \right)^{T_c/T}$$

for

$$C \approx \frac{K}{4\pi L} 10^{-12} \text{ farads/cm}^2$$

From equation 4.16, the space charge-limited current follows immediately, using for the electric field the approximation V/L:

$$I = (V/L)ne\mu$$

$$= N_ce\mu \left(\frac{K10^{-12}}{4\pi ekT_cA} \right)^{T_c/T} L^{-[2(T_c/T)+1]} V^{(T_c/T)+1} \qquad (4.17)$$

Equation 4.17 shows that the current increases as the $(T_c +$

$T)/T$ power of the voltage and even faster, namely, as the $[2(T_c/T) + 1]$ power of the reciprocal spacing L. While the high power dependency of current on voltage has been frequently observed, it is only recently that the concomitant high power dependence on electrode spacing was confirmed by H. P. D. Lanyon.*

4.3 Field and Charge Distribution

In Section 4.2, the assumption was made that the injected charge was uniformly distributed in the space between cathode and anode. We show here that this approximation becomes increasingly good, the steeper the current–voltage curve.

The equations to be resolved are the Poisson equation

$$\frac{d\mathcal{E}}{dx} = \frac{4\pi e}{K}\,(n + n_t) \tag{4.18}$$

and the equation for current

$$I = ne\mu\mathcal{E} \tag{4.19}$$

where $\mathcal{E}$ is the electric field and n and n_t the free and trapped components of the injected charge density, respectively

We assume that $n_t \gg n$ so that the free-carrier density can be neglected in equation 4.18. Also, from equation 4.16 we take

$$n = BV^m \doteq B_1 n_t{}^m \tag{4.20}$$

where $m = T_c/T$ and $B_1 = B(eL/C)^m$. With these conditions, equation 4.18 becomes

$$\frac{d\mathcal{E}}{dx} = \frac{4\pi e}{K}\left(\frac{n}{B_1}\right)^{1/m}$$

$$= \frac{4\pi e}{K}\left(\frac{I}{B_1 e\mu\mathcal{E}}\right)^{1/m} = R\mathcal{E}^{-1/m} \tag{4.21}$$

---

* Reported at the Conference on Space Charge Effects in Dielectrics, Westhampton, L. I., June 15, 1962. Also, *Phys. Rev.*, **130**, 134 (1963).

where

$$R \equiv \frac{4\pi e}{K} \left(\frac{I}{B_1 e \mu} \right)^{1/m}$$

The solution of equation 4.21 is

$$\mathcal{E} = \left(\frac{m+1}{m} Rx \right)^{m/(m+1)} \tag{4.22}$$

For $m = 1$ we have the case of free or free-plus-shallow traps for which

$$\mathcal{E} \propto x^{1/2} \tag{4.23}$$

For $m \to \infty$, we have the case of deep traps with a steep current–voltage curve for which

$$\mathcal{E} \propto x \tag{4.24}$$

The charge distribution is from equations 4.18 and 4.22

$$en_t = \frac{K}{4\pi} \frac{d\mathcal{E}}{dx}$$

$$= \left(\frac{m+1}{m} \right)^{-1/(m+1)} R^{m/(m+1)} x^{-1/(m+1)}$$

$$= \text{Const. } x^{-1/(m+1)} \tag{4.25}$$

For the free or free-plus-shallow trap cases, $m = 1$ and

$$en_t \propto x^{-1/2} \tag{4.26}$$

For the case of deep traps, $m > 1$ and

$$en_t \propto x^{-1/(m+1)} \tag{4.27}$$

Equation 4.27 supports the approximation that the charge is uniformly distributed between cathode and anode since as $m \to \infty$, $en_t \to$ constant.

4.4   Transient Effects

There are several transient effects that are both characteristic of space-charge current flow and valuable experimental tools for measuring transit times and trapping times.

When the voltage is first applied across a sample, free carriers rush into the conduction band from the reservoir at the cathode. The steady current and space-charge pattern are established in one or two transit times if there are no traps. The transit time is likely to be 10^{-8} sec or shorter for 100 volts applied across a sample 10^{-3} cm thick. If we now perform the same experiment in the presence of traps, but assume that the trapping time is longer than the transit time, we should expect the initial current to be that appropriate to free carriers in the absence of traps. As time goes on, the initial current will decay to the steady-state value appropriate to the presence of traps. In some cases, as in Smith's original observations (Fig. 4.4) on single crystals of CdS, the ratio of trap-free currents to trap-controlled currents is found to be many powers of ten. The transient currents are strikingly large compared with the steady-state currents. In these experiments the initial current was used to measure the trap-free drift mobility. The rate of decay of the initial current was used to measure the trapping time as well as the capture cross section of the traps.

The same experiment was used by Mark to measure trapping times in anthracene. Mark added the further check of measuring the rate of thermal release from traps by observing how long after the first pulse voltage was applied, the pulse could be reapplied with the same high transient current. The waiting time was a measure of the rate of thermal release of electrons trapped during the first transient.

The observation of a high transient current which decays to a small or negligible steady current is reminiscent of the phenomenon of "dielectric absorption." In the latter case, as in the well-known Leyden jar experiment, reverse currents and voltages comparable with the applied voltage are observed when the

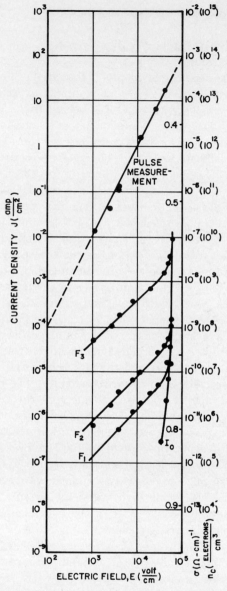

Fig. 4.4. Pulsed (top curve) and steady-state space-charge-limited current-voltage curves for CdS in the dark I_o and under increasing illumination $F_1 - F_3$. Crystal thickness: 2.5×10^{-3} cm. (Taken from R. W. Smith.)

sample is shorted. It is in this respect that space-charge currents depart markedly from "dielectric absorption." The short circuit currents observed from a sample into which space charge has been previously injected is likely to be negligibly small. The space charge (see Fig. 4.5) flows out almost symmetrically from *both* ends of the sample.

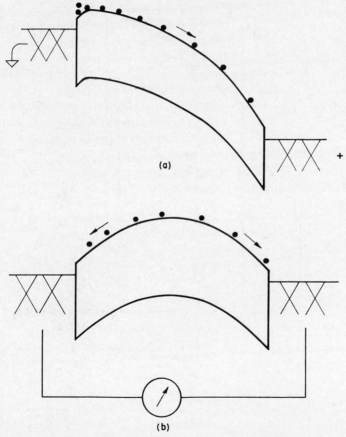

(a)

+

(b)

Fig. 4.5. Effect of short circuiting a solid carrrying a space-charge-limited current. (a) Under applied voltage, (b) short circuited.

A particularly elegant use of the transient current was proposed independently by Many and by Helfrich and Mark. Many used it to measure the drift mobility in crystals of iodine; Helfrich and Mark did the same for anthracene, using electrically Ohmic contacts. Silver made similar observations on anthracene using photoelectrically generated Ohmic contacts. Both Many and Mark and Helfrich showed analytically that the initial transient current should have a cusp (see Fig. 4.6) at about $0.8\ t_0$, where t_0 is the transit time in a uniform field. The cusp arises because at $t = 0$, the space charge injected in the crystal is less than can be accommodated in the steady state. At times small compared with a transit time, the space charge is localized near the cathode and its magnitude is given by the simple condenser relation for charge localized at the two electrodes. In one transit time the space charge spreads through the sample, giving a distributed charge for which the capacitance is approximately doubled. The leading front of the space charge arrives at the anode in a time shorter than the uniform-field transit time, because the average field that the first front sees

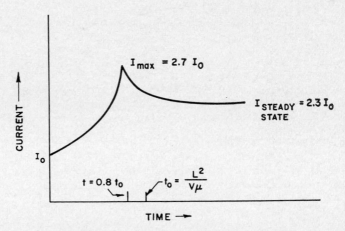

Fig. 4.6. Starting transient of space-charge-limited current flow (as analyzed by A. Many and by P. Mark and W. Helfrich).

during its transit is higher than the uniform field, owing to the increased capacitance of the distributed charge. The current, when the first front arrives at the anode, is higher than its steady-state value because at that time there is more space charge in the crystal than in the steady state. This comes about because when the first front arrives the space charge is weighted more heavily near the anode than it is in the steady state. The combination of the above transient effects gives a cusp to the current-versus-time curve at 0.8 times the uniform field transit time. This cusp persists even in the presence of trapping and offers a well-defined fiduciary mark for measuring drift transit times and drift mobilities. Both Many and Mark and Helfrich have carried out a detailed analysis of the current transient and have confirmed the analysis with experimental data on iodine and anthracene, respectively.

References

Fan, H. Y., *Phys. Rev.*, **74**, 1505 (1948).

Helfrich, W., and P. Mark, *Z. Physik*, **166**, 370 (1962).

Lampert, M. A., *Phys. Rev.*, **103**, 1648 (1956).

Lampert, M. A., A. Rose, and R. W. Smith, *J. Phys. Chem. Solids*, **8**, 464 (1959).

Many, A., and G. Rakavy, *Phys. Rev.*, **126**, 1980 (1962).

Many, A., Simhony, M., Weiss, S. Z., and Levinson, J., *Photoconductivity*, Pergamon Press, New York, 1962, p. 285.

Many, A., S. Z. Weiss, and J. Levinson, *Phys. Rev.*, **126**, 1989 (1962).

Mark, P., and W. Helfrich, *J. Appl. Phys.*, **33**, 205 (1962).

Mott, N. F., and R. W. Gurney, *Electronic Processes in Ionic Crystals*, Oxford University Press, New York, 1940, p. 172.

Rose, A., *Phys. Rev.*, **97**, 1538 (1955).

Ruppel, W., *Helv. Phys. Acta*, **31**, 311 (1958).

Silver, M., M. Swicord, R. C. Jarnigan, A. Many, S. Z. Weiss, and M. Simhony, *J. Phys. Chem. Solids*, **23**, 419 (1962).

Smith, R. W., *RCA Rev.*, **20**, 69 (1959).

Smith, R. W., and A. Rose, *Phys. Rev.*, **97**, 1531 (1955).

Stöckmann, F., *Halbleiterprobleme*, Vol. VI, Friedr. Vieweg und Sohn, Braunschweig, Germany. Edited by W. Schottky. 1961, p. 279.

Wright, G. T., *Nature*, **182**, 1296 (1958).

Chapter 5

Gain–Bandwidth Product—Part II

5.1 Trap-Free and Shallow Trap Photoconductors

In Chapter 3 we discussed at some length the lifetime of free carriers. The lifetime of a free carrier gives the total optically excited number of free carriers by the relation,

$$\mathfrak{N} = F\tau \tag{2.1}$$

From equation 2.1 we obtain the photocurrent

$$I = \mathfrak{N}e/T_r \tag{2.2}$$

and since the transit time T_r is inversely proportional to the applied voltage, we expect the photocurrent to be proportional to the applied voltage.

Figure 5.1 shows a photoconductor under illumination first with no applied voltage and then with both a low and a somewhat higher applied voltage. We show these elementary figures to emphasize the role played by the Ohmic or reservoir type of contact. At successively higher applied voltages the Ohmic contact adjusts itself via its virtual cathode to supply as many carriers as their rate of transport through the volume calls for. A more detailed discussion of the Ohmic contact will be found in Chapter 8.

A second feature of the Ohmic contact at low voltages is that the condenser charge due to the applied voltage lies close to the contact itself and has negligible extent through the bulk of the photoconductor. This is not altogether obvious and, in fact,

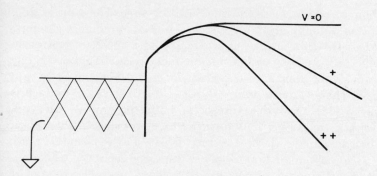

Fig. 5.1. Potential distribution near an Ohmic contact for a range of applied voltages.

no longer true at higher voltages. The condenser charge lies in the virtual cathode and is being pulled by the field into the volume of the photoconductor. What keeps it from spreading throughout the volume? One simple and instructive way of looking at the problem is to say that the charge at the cathode is being continuously drawn into the volume and continuously dissipated by dielectric relaxation.

Consider, for example, an element of volume near the middle of the photoconductor. Let it charge up negatively to whatever equilibrium value it would have in the absence of dielectric relaxation. The time required for charging is the transit time from cathode to the middle of the photoconductor. Now let the charge be dissipated by dielectric relaxation for a time equal to the transit time. If the dielectric relaxation time is short compared with the transit time, the fraction of charge remaining will be negligibly small, namely, $\exp(-T_r/\tau_{\mathrm{rel}})$.

We have separated the supply and relaxation of charge into two successive processes to emphasize their competitive character. Actually, the two processes go on simultaneously. The result is quantitatively closely approximated by the successive processes. The result is that negligible space charge appears in the volume of the photoconductor for transit times large compared with the dielectric relaxation time. The same is true, of course, for any Ohmic resistor as well as for photoconductors. When the transit time approximates the dielectric relaxation time, the condenser charge does, in fact, spread from the cathode through the volume of the photoconductor very much as in a space-charge-limited vacuum diode. Further, as the voltage is increased beyond this threshold, both the transit time and dielectric relaxation time decrease together, since the increased voltage increases the free carrier density in the volume. Figure 5.2 shows the variation of transit time and dielectric relaxation time with applied voltage for a trap-free solid. The voltage at which the two times become equal is the threshold voltage for the onset of space-charge-limited currents.

We show now that the condition for the equality of transit and dielectric relaxation time is also the condition for doubling the free-carrier density in the volume of a trap-free photoconductor. We begin with

$$T_r = \tau_{\text{rel}} \tag{5.1}$$

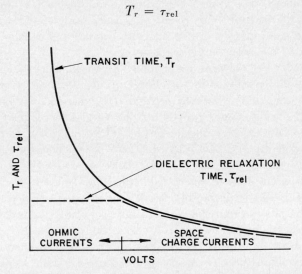

Fig. 5.2. Variation of transit time and dielectric relaxation time with applied voltage (trap-free solid).

or

$$\frac{L^2}{V\mu} = \frac{K}{4\pi ne\mu} \times 10^{-12} \tag{5.2}$$

and rearrange equation 5.2 as follows:

$$neL = \frac{KV}{4\pi L} \times 10^{-12} \tag{5.3}$$

The left side of equation 5.3 is the total number of free-carrier "charges" in the photoconductor, while the right side is the condenser charge (product of voltage and capacitance) forced into the volume of the photoconductor by the applied voltage.

From the above argument (see also Fig. 5.2), we can write the gain of a photoconductor in the range of space-charge current flow:

$$G = \frac{\tau}{T_r} = \frac{\tau_0}{\tau_{\text{rel}}} \tag{5.4a}$$

or

$$G\frac{1}{\tau_0} = \frac{1}{\tau_{\text{rel}}} \tag{5.4b}$$

In equation 5.4, the response time τ_0 is equal to the lifetime τ, since we have not introduced traps.

If we introduce shallow traps, equation 5.4a is still valid by the following argument. The introduction of shallow traps increases the voltage at which space-charge flow sets in by the factor n_t/n, since the density of trapped carriers as well as of free carriers must be doubled by the injected charge. Thus, at the onset of space-charge flow, $T_r = (n/n_t)\tau_{\text{rel}}$, and we write

$$G = \frac{\tau}{T_r} = \frac{\tau}{\tau_{\text{rel}}(n/n_t)} = \frac{\tau_0}{\tau_{\text{rel}}} \tag{5.5a}$$

or

$$G\frac{1}{\tau_0} = \frac{1}{\tau_{\text{rel}}} \tag{5.5b}$$

where G is the gain at the onset of space-charge flow and τ_0 is the response time for the case of shallow traps. The same form of gain–bandwidth product is valid for both the trap-free and shallow-trap cases.

5.2   Photoconductors with Deep Traps

It remains to explore the effect of deep traps (i.e., below the Fermi level) and of recombination centers on the gain–bandwidth product. The effect of deep traps is shown schematically in Figure 5.3. Here we have applied in the dark, sufficient

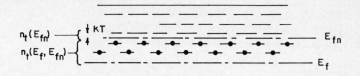

Fig. 5.3. Definition of $n_t(E_f, E_{fn})$ and $n_t(E_f)$.

voltage to raise the Fermi level from its dark value E_f to a higher steady-state value, E_{fn}. In the process, the states lying between E_f and E_{fn} had to be filled with electrons by the applied voltage. For a density of trapping states large compared with the density of free carriers, the voltage needed to raise the Fermi level by injection of space charge is equal to

$$V = \frac{n_t(E_f, E_{fn})eL}{C} \tag{5.6}$$

where $n_t(E_f, E_{fn})$ refers to all the trapping states lying between E_f and E_{fn}.

If we now introduce a small amount of light so that the

free-carrier density is perturbed but not more than doubled, we wll find that the response time is given by

$$\tau_0 = \frac{n_t(E_{fn})}{n} \tau \qquad (5.7)$$

where $n_t(E_{fn})$ is the density of traps in a kT-wide slice at E_{fn}. From equations 5.6 and 5.7 it is seen that the effect of having filled the deep traps in the interval $|E_f, E_{fn}|$ is to decrease the transit time (at the onset of space-charge flow) over that appropriate to free carriers alone by the factor

$$\frac{n}{n_t(E_f, E_{fn})} \qquad (5.8)$$

and to increase the response time by the factor

$$\frac{n_t(E_{fn})}{n} \qquad (5.9)$$

The net effect is

$$G = \frac{\tau}{T_r} = \frac{\tau_0 \dfrac{n}{n_t(E_{fn})}}{\tau_{rel} \dfrac{n}{n_t(E_f, E_{fn})}} \qquad (5.10)$$

$$= \frac{\tau_0}{\tau_{rel}} \frac{n_t(E_f, E_{fn})}{n_t(E_{fn})} = \frac{\tau_0}{\tau_{rel}} M$$

where

$$M = \frac{n_t(E_f, E_{fn})}{n_t(E_{fn})} \qquad (5.11)$$

The factor M may be looked upon in several ways, one of which is the ratio of deep to shallow traps as just discussed. A second way is obtained by recognizing $n_t(E_f, E_{fn})eL$ as the anode charge required to fill the deep traps. At the same time $n_t(E_{fn})eL$ is the total "charge" in thermal equilibrium or thermal contact with the conduction band. Hence M can be defined as the ratio of these two quantities. This was the physical picture presented by Rose and Lampert. A third way of regarding M was derived by Redington, namely, as the ratio of the differential to the secant resistance at the operating point. The differential resistance (see Fig. 5.4) may be written in the form of finite differences for the operation of doubling the current:

$$\frac{\Delta I}{\Delta V} = \frac{IC}{n_t(E_{fn})eL} \tag{5.12}$$

where $\Delta V = n_t(E_{fn})eL/C$ is the increase in voltage required to double the current. The secant resistance is (using eq. 5.6)

$$\frac{I}{V} = \frac{IC}{en_t(E_f, E_{fn})L} \tag{5.13}$$

The ratio of equation 5.12 to 5.13 is

$$\frac{\Delta I}{\Delta V} \bigg/ \frac{I}{V} = \frac{n_t(E_f, E_{fn})}{n_t(E_{fn})} = M \tag{5.14}$$

and confirms Redington's definition of M.

There is still a fourth way of regarding M which is instruc-

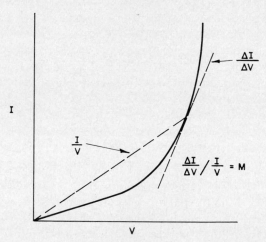

Fig. 5.4. Comparison of differential and secant resistances.

tive. Note that in the above illustration (Fig. 5.3), we chose to raise the Fermi level from E_f to E_{fn} by first applying a voltage in the dark sufficient to inject the appropriate trap-filling space charge. We then perturbed the dark current by photoexcitation. We chose a perturbation rather than a large change in order to retain the space-charge-limited flow condition. This method of operation is unsatisfactory for most applications because a high M value means a steeply rising current–voltage curve (see Redington's definition of M) and all of its attendant instabilities.

Suppose, in place of first applying the voltage, we were to raise the Fermi level from E_f to E_{fn} by first applying the light. The result would be to incorporate the states in the interval (E_f, E_{fn}) into the category of recombination states as discussed in Chapter 3. [We called these states traps under the conditions of first applying the voltage because in the absence of light there are no recombination states defined and all empty states become electron traps for the injected space charge.] If, now, we apply a voltage to the photoconductor we will observe Ohm's law for voltages up to the value required to fill the states in the (E_f, E_{fn}) interval (see Fig. 4.4). Consider the situation for voltages just short of threshold for space-charge injection. On the one hand, we would expect the same M value as before since by the Rose-Lampert criterion the ratio of charge on the anode to charge in thermal contact with the conduction band is the same. On the other hand, the Redington criterion does not apply since we are dealing with Ohmic currents. [If Redington's criterion were applied, it would give $M = 1$]. The appropriate definition of M under these conditions would be the ratio of empty recombination centers to electron-occupied states in thermal contact with the conduction band. This is numerically equal to the Rose-Lampert criterion and also to the first concept introduced above, namely, the ratio of deep to shallow traps. The awkward ambiguity comes about because the states $n_t(E_f, E_{fn})$ are treated as traps when the voltage is applied first and as recombination centers when the light is applied first. Both concepts are proper in their context.

One conclusion from this discussion is that the Rose-Lampert interpretation of M probably has the more general validity. It is valid both for space-charge flow and for Ohmic currents, for either order in which light and voltage are applied, and for the continuous range of voltages down to zero volts. It is valid also for the interpretation of the M value of the phototransistor.

We should not fail to note that while we arrived at the same M value in both examples of first applying the voltage or first applying the light, we did not arrive at the same photocurrent or photosensitivity. When the voltage was applied first and a perturbation by light introduced, the electron lifetime was given by

$$\tau_n = \frac{1}{n_t(E_f)vs_n} \tag{5.15}$$

When the light was applied first and the voltage raised to a value just short of space-charge injection, the electron lifetime was

$$\tau_n = \frac{1}{n_t(E_f, E_{fn})vs_n} \tag{5.16}$$

In brief, there would appear to be a discontinuous or, at least, a very rapid increase of photosensitivity by a factor numerically equal to M as one passes from Ohmic to space-charge flow.

5.3 Effect of Trapping Times Larger than Lifetimes

Throughout our discussion of the effect of traps on response time, we have assumed that the trapped electrons were in "thermal contact with the free electrons," namely, that an electron was trapped in a time shorter than its lifetime. It was, however, noted in Section 3.3 that when the time required to trap a free electron exceeded its lifetime by more than several-fold, the material responded to changes in light intensity almost like a trap-free material. That is, the response time approached the lifetime of a free electron. On the other hand, the effect of traps in postponing the onset of space charge-limited currents is independent of their capture cross sections. We have here at least a formal possibility of departing from the symmetric and self-canceling effects of traps on transit time and response time pointed out in Section 5.1. The magnitude of this departure is of the order of the ratio of trapped to free carriers and should appear as an M factor of the same value.

This means for achieving large M factors is not likely to be significant for sensitive photoconductors where, by definition, the lifetime is large and likely to be many-fold larger than the time needed to trap a free carrier. It could however, play a significant role in properly tailored insensitive photoconductors.*

5.4   N-P-N Junction Photocell

The N-P-N junction photocell (Fig. 5.5) represents a particularly useful way of achieving M values in excess of unity. The N-P-N junction is also a convenient conceptual bridge between normal solid-state triode amplifiers and photoconductors regarded as amplifiers.

The photoconductive gain of an N-P-N junction is the ratio of the transit time of an electron through the base or P section to the lifetime of a free pair in that section. This follows from the concepts of photoconductive gain used already in Chapter 1. Hence, we write

$$G = \tau/T_r \qquad (5.17)$$

The photoconductive response time can, in the perturbation case, be computed by asking for the time required for a steady-

---

* H. S. Sommers, Jr., has analyzed the performance of devices using photoconducting insulators with one contact floating (e.g., Vidicon, Electrofax, Xerography) to show that significant increases in gain can be obtained when the time for a carrier to be trapped exceeds its recombination lifetime, JAP (in press).

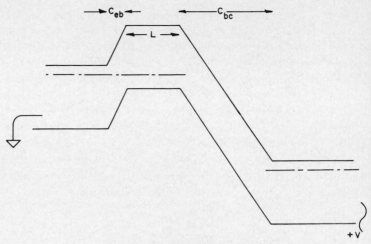

Fig. 5.5. *N-P-N* phototransistor.

state light to double the current through the junction. This is at least the lifetime for free pairs in the P section. The light required per square centimeter of device cross section is given by

$$F = nL/\tau \qquad (5.18)$$

However, when the free-electron density in the P section is doubled, the potential jump between emitter and base must be decreased by about kT/e to fit the new equilibrium. The light must hence supply the appropriate charge across the emitter–base depletion layer to effect this potential change. We neglect for simplicity the base–collector capacitance, which should, in any event, become negligible at collector voltages large compared with the contact potential between the N and P sections. The additional charge is

$$(kT/e)C_{eb}$$

and the total response time is

$$\tau_0 = \tau + \frac{kTC_{eb}}{e^2F} = \tau\left(1 + \frac{kTC_{eb}}{e^2nL}\right) \qquad (5.19)$$

If we now try to optimize the performance of the N-P-N junction, we see that a reduction in L of the P section shortens the transit time and hence improves the gain. At the same time the response time by equation 5.19 is unchanged so long as $e^2 nL > kTC_{eb}$. Suppose we reduce L until the dominant term in the response time is $(kTC_{eb}/e^2 nL)$, the time needed to charge the geometric capacitance between emitter and base. Under these conditions, equation 5.19 becomes

$$\tau_0 = \frac{kTC_{eb}}{e^2 nL} \tau \qquad (5.20)$$

With equation 5.20, the definition of gain (eq. 5.17) becomes

$$G = \frac{\tau_0 neL}{T_r(kT/e)C_{eb}} = \frac{\tau_0}{R_{kT}C_{eb}} \qquad (5.21)$$

where

$$R_{kT} \equiv \frac{kT/e}{neL/T_r} = \frac{kT/e}{I}$$

is the resistance for a voltage of kT/e applied across the N-P-N junction. Rearrangement of equation 5.21 gives the gain–bandwidth product

$$G\frac{1}{\tau_0} = \frac{1}{R_{kT}C_{eb}} \qquad (5.22)$$

Equation 5.22 has the same form as that obtained in Section 5.1 for a normal photoconductor. In fact, it is identical for applied voltages not exceeding kT/e. For larger applied voltages, the resistance of the device, whether it is measured as the collector voltage divided by the collector current or as a differential resistance, rapidly exceeds the value R_{kT}. Meantime, the gain, for a fixed L, does not change nor does the response time. Hence, equation 5.22 holds for voltages larger than kT/e as well. But R_{kT} does not describe the resistance of the device at the higher voltages and we need to replace it with a larger value. This means that a factor $M > 1$ must be introduced in the numerator to keep the right side of equation 5.22 constant.

The following is a formal replacement of $R_{kT}C_{eb}$ by the RC of the base–collector region at voltages large compared with kT/e. We choose to measure R at these higher voltages by the ratio of collector voltage to collector current. Also, we make the approximation that the collector current is saturated at voltages greater than kT/e. Hence,

$$R_V \equiv \frac{V}{I} = \frac{Ve}{kT} R_{kT} \qquad (5.23)$$

Also, at voltages larger than V_0, the contact potential between the P and N sections, the base–collector capacitance is

$$C_{bc} = \left(\frac{V_0}{V}\right)^{1/2} C_{eb} \qquad (5.24)$$

From equations 5.23 and 5.24 we can write

$$R_{kT}C_{eb} = R_V C_{bc} \frac{kT}{e(VV_0)^{1/2}} \qquad (5.25)$$

Finally, insertion of equation 5.25 into equation 5.22 gives

$$G \frac{1}{\tau_0} = \frac{1}{R_V C_{bc}} M \qquad (5.26)$$

where

$$M = \frac{(VV_0)^{1/2}}{kT/e}$$

For $V = 10$ volts and $V_0 = 1$ volt, $M = 100$ at room temperature.

5.5 Comparison of Photoconductor Amplifiers and Solid-State Triode Amplifiers

The mechanism for current gain in a solid-state triode amplifier is essentially the same as in a photoconductor (see, for example, Johnson and Rose). In both cases an extra carrier is introduced into the space between emitter and collector for a time τ which is longer than its transit time T_r so that a current gain of τ/T_r is obtained. In the case of solid-state triodes (and vacuum triodes), the general relation was obtained for the current gain–bandwidth product (see Johnson and Rose, 1959).

$$G\Delta B = \frac{1}{2\pi T_r} \tag{5.27}$$

where T_r was the transit time between emitter and grid. The transit time from grid to collector is, in general, shorter than that between emitter and grid. Now, it is true that for most, if not all, of the solid-state triodes the significant transit time for best operation is across an element of space in which there is either an exhaustion layer or space charge-limited current flow or the voltage is at threshold for space-charge flow. We have shown that the transit time becomes equal to the RC time constant (τ_{rel}) under trap-free, space charge-limited flow. The transit time across an exhaustion layer is, in the absence of saturated drift velocity, also equal to the RC time constant of the semiconductor before formation of the exhaustion layer. This follows because the same value of electric field is required to either exhaust or double a given density of carriers in a given volume. In brief, there is good reason to write equation 5.27 for solid-state triodes in the form

$$G\Delta B = \frac{1}{2\pi RC} \tag{5.28}$$

where the RC is evaluated in the emitter–grid space but not in the grid–collector space.

Equation 5.28 has the same form as equation 2.19 for photoconductors except that equation 5.28 lacks the factor M. Since the physics of the gain process is the same in both types of devices, it is natural to ask why the M factor is present for one and not the other. This comes about when we recognize that the τ_{rel} for a photoconductor is evaluated throughout the homogeneous space between emitter and collector. The photoconductor has, in effect, a distributed grid, owing to the uniform absorption of light in the space between emitter and grid. The τ_{rel} or RC time for the solid-state triode, on the other hand, is evaluated in the emitter–grid space and not in the grid–collector space. This can be done since the grid is localized. If the τ_{rel} were evaluated for the triode in the grid–collector space, it would be found to be much larger than in the emitter–grid space and an M factor would have to be introduced to reduce it to the latter for which equation 5.28 is valid.

The transition from photoconductor-like conditions to triode-like conditions can readily be seen in the N-P-N junction photocell. For an applied voltage of kT/e, the τ_{rel} of both emitter–grid and grid–collector spaces are substantially the same and the M factor is unity. For applied voltages larger than kT/e, an M factor greater than unity was introduced because the τ_{rel} was evaluated in the grid–collector space where it steadily increases with applied voltage while the performance of the device meantime remained substantially unchanged. It is proper to use the τ_{rel} of the grid–collector space rather than the emitter–grid space even in the N-P-N junction where one has a choice, because the operation of a number of significant photodevices depend on the τ_{rel} or leakage currents in the grid–collector space.

References

DeVore, H. B., *RCA Rev.*, **20**, 79 (1959).
Johnson, E. O., and A. Rose, *Proc. IRE*, **47**, 407 (1959).
Redington, R. W., *J. Appl. Phys.*, **29**, 189 (1958).
Redington, R. W., *Phys. Rev.*, **115**, 894 (1959).
Rose, A., *L'Onde Electrique*, **34**, 645 (1956).
Rose, A., *Helv. Phys. Acta*, **30**, 242 (1957).
Rose, A., and M. A. Lampert, *Phys. Rev.*, **113**, 1227 (1959).
Rose, A., and M. A. Lampert, *RCA Rev.*, **20**, 57 (1959).
Smith, R. W., *RCA Rev.*, **20**, 69 (1959).
Stöckmann, F., in R. G. Breckenridge, B. R. Russell, and E. E. Hahn, eds., *Photoconductivity Conference*, Wiley, New York–London, 1954, p. 269.
Stöckmann, F., *Z. Physik*, **147**, 544 (1957).

Chapter 6

Noise Currents

6.1 General Formalism

We use here a formalism for computing noise currents based on simple particle arguments rather than on the usual Fourier analysis of the current pulses of individual electrons. The writer has found the formalism useful for visualizing the physical origin of noise and for making comparisons of noise currents from diverse sources.

Consider a stream F/sec of randomly spaced events laid out in a line as in Figure 6.1. Let us divide the stream into equal time intervals which we regard as the smallest resolvable element of time dictated either by the physics of the process at hand or by our arbitrary choice. The interval τ will be recognized as related to the bandwidth of our system by

$$\tau = 1/2\Delta B \qquad (6.1)$$

Each interval of time contains on the average $\bar{n}$ events.

The stream of events may be photons, electrons, excitations, etc. such that each event makes an observable contribution. We define the observed current as the product of the stream of events and the charge contribution per event and write the current as

$$I = \frac{\text{av. number of events in interval } \tau}{\tau}$$

$$\times \text{ charge contribution per event} \qquad (6.2)$$

$$= \frac{\bar{n}}{\tau}\,\alpha$$

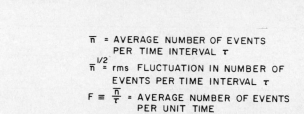

$\bar{n}$ = AVERAGE NUMBER OF EVENTS PER TIME INTERVAL τ

$\bar{n}^{1/2}$ = rms FLUCTUATION IN NUMBER OF EVENTS PER TIME INTERVAL τ

$F \equiv \dfrac{\bar{n}}{\tau}$ = AVERAGE NUMBER OF EVENTS PER UNIT TIME

Fig. 6.1. Formalism for analysis of noise currents.

where α is the contribution per event. The reason for this elementary formulation is to compare the average current I with the noise current I_n in easily visualizable terms.

The average number of events, $\bar{n}$, per interval will have associated with it, by the well-known statistical relation, a root mean squared fluctuation $\bar{n}^{1/2}$. The root mean squared noise current can then be written in the same form as the average current, namely,

$$I_n = \frac{\text{rms fluctuation in average number of particles per interval } \tau}{\tau}$$

$\times$ charge contribution per event   (6.3)

$$= \frac{\bar{n}^{1/2}}{\tau}\,\alpha$$

or, for the mean-squared noise current

$$I_n{}^2 = \frac{\bar{n}\alpha^2}{\tau^2}$$

$$= \frac{F\alpha^2}{\tau} \tag{6.4}$$

$$= 2F\alpha^2\Delta B \tag{6.5}$$

In this formalism we have taken α, the contribution per event, to be a non-fluctuating parameter. When α itself has fluctuations, these must, of course, be added to the noise. At most, the correction is a factor of 2 in the mean-squared noise current for the problems considered here. An example of a constant α are the charge pulses of electrons in a vacuum photocell. An example of a fluctuating α requiring a factor of 2 correction (as discussed in Section 6.5) are the charge pulses contributed by electrons excited into the conduction band. The fluctuations in lifetime of a free electron have a mean-squared spread equal to the average lifetime itself. An example of a minor fluctuation in α are the charge pulses contributed in the output of a photomultiplier by individual electrons from the photocathode. The correction factor is approximately $1 + 1/r$, where r is the secondary emission of the first stage.

Since equation 6.5 is linear in the bandwidth, the mean-squared noise current per unit bandwidth is a constant, $2F\alpha^2$. Or, as is frequently stated, the noise spectrum is flat from zero frequency to the limit of resolution set by the phenomenon or system of observation, whichever cuts off first.

We apply the formalism of equation 6.5 to a number of noise problems to derive some well-known results before treating the less familiar problem of noise currents in the presence of traps.

6.2 Photon Currents

For a stream $F/\sec$ of independent photons striking a receiver, the mean-squared fluctuation in the current of photons is, by equation 6.5:

$$F_n{}^2 = 2F\Delta B \qquad (6.6)$$

The factor α, the contribution per event, is unity, namely, one photon.

6.3 Emission-Limited Currents

The mean-squared fluctuations in an emission-limited current of electrons such as one might have in a vacuum photocell or in a temperature-limited diode is, by equation 6.5,

$$I_n{}^2 = 2e^2F\Delta B$$
$$= 2eI\Delta B$$

where F is the number of electrons emitted per second and eF is the corresponding measured electrical current I. The contribution per event here is e, the charge on an electron.

6.4 Photomultipliers

Let the input or primary current of electrons in a photomultiplier be F/sec and let the multiplier gain be G. Then, the contribution per event is Ge and the mean-squared fluctuation in *output* current is

$$[I_n{}^2]_{\text{out}} = 2F(eG)^2\Delta B$$
$$= 2eI_{\text{in}}G^2\Delta B \qquad (6.7)$$
$$= 2eI_{\text{out}}G\Delta B$$

where I_{in} ($= eF$) is the input current and I_{out} ($= GI_{\text{in}}$) is the output current. We have ignored here the small fluctuations in G referred to in Section 6.1.

6.5 Photoconductor (Trap-Free)

Let an incident light flux give rise to a total of F excitations per second in a trap-free photoconductor and let the photoconductor have a gain G. This means that each event (or excitation) gives rise, on the average, to a charge Ge in the external circuit. Since the termination, as well as the initiation, of the life of a free electron is a random process, there is an equal source of noise contributed by the random processes of the recombination traffic. The mean-squared noise current is then

$$I_n{}^2 = 4F(Ge)^2\Delta B$$
$$= 4eIG\Delta B \qquad (6.8)$$

where I is the measured photocurrent, taken to be large compared with the dark current and, by equation 2.3, is equal to eFG. The noise currents for a photoconductor and photomultiplier having equal gains and quantum yields differ only by a factor of 2. This is the factor of 2 arising from fluctuations in the α of the photoconductor. A more significant difference between the two devices is that the bandwidth ΔB is more seriously restricted in a photoconductor. Since a gain of G in a photoconductor requires one lifetime to be completed, ΔB cannot be chosen larger than $(2\tau)^{-1}$, where τ is the lifetime of a free carrier. In the photomultiplier, the shortest resolvable time is less than or equal to the transit time of an electron through the multiplier and is set ultimately by the spread in transit times. Note also in equation 6.8 that the total integrated noise for a given current is independent of the gain, since the product of G and ΔB is a constant equal to one half the reciprocal transit time. The noise per unit bandwidth is, of course, proportional to the gain.

Suppose we shine light on the photoconductor and measure the noise current of the excited carriers in the absence of an applied field. Again we have a total of F excitations per second. The charge contribution of each excited carrier to the external circuit is now, on the average,

$$eL_D/L \tag{6.9}$$

where L_D is the distance a free carrier diffuses during its lifetime and L is the separation of electrodes.

We are using here for simplicity a one-dimensional argument and say that, on the average, half the displacements are to the right and half to the left. The mean-squared fluctuation in number of displacements to the right is then equal to the average number, that is, half the total events. We add the mean-squared fluctuation in number of displacements to the right and to the left and obtain the total number of events. This argument is used to show that we can use the same formalism as given in equation 6.5 even though the displacements average out to zero. The mean-squared noise current then becomes

$$I_n{}^2 = 4F \left(e \frac{L_D}{L} \right)^2 \Delta B \qquad (6.10)$$

where the extra factor of 2 comes from the equal contribution of recombination processes to the noise current.

We know from diffusion theory that

$$L_D{}^2 = D\tau$$

$$= \frac{kT}{e} \mu\tau \qquad (6.11)$$

Inserting this value of $L_D{}^2$ into equation 6.10, we get

$$I_n{}^2 = 4 \frac{eF\tau\mu}{L^2} kT\Delta B$$

$$= 4 \frac{e\mathfrak{N}\mu}{L^2} kT\Delta B \qquad (6.12)$$

$$= 4 \frac{kT}{R} \Delta B$$

since $e\mathfrak{N}\mu/L^2 = 1/R$, the resistance of the photoconductor, $\mathfrak{N}$ being the total number of photoexcited carriers. Equation 6.12 is, of course, interesting in that it is just the expression for Johnson or thermal agitation noise.

Since equation 6.12 is valid at zero applied voltage and equation 6.8 at a sufficiently large applied voltage, we ask at what voltage the transition occurs. Actually, it is a critical field (Fig. 6.2) at which the photoconductor noise current exceeds the Johnson value (both referred to the low-pass bandwidth of the photoconductor) and becomes field dependent. This field is readily computed by comparing the "contribution per event" for the two cases. For an applied field, $\mathcal{E}$, it is

$$eG = e \frac{\mathcal{E}\mu\tau}{L} \qquad (6.13)$$

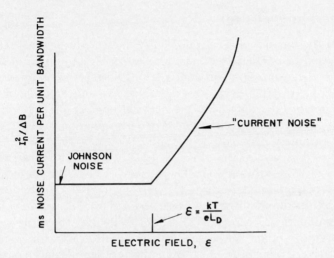

Fig. 6.2. Noise current in a photoconductor or resistor as a function of electric field (L_D = diffusion length).

and for zero applied field it is

$$eG = e \frac{L_D}{L}$$
$$= e \frac{kT\mu\tau}{eL_D L}$$

(6.14)

where from equation 6.11, $L_D = (kT/eL_D)\mu\tau$.

From equations 6.13 and 6.14 it is clear that the photocurrent noise of equation 6.8 will begin to be dominant when the applied field is greater than the effective diffusion field, namely,

$$\varepsilon > \frac{kT}{eL_D}$$

(6.15)

Since L_D is usually in the range of one micron to about 10^3 microns, the transition field will be in the range of 10^{-1} to 10^2 volts/cm for $kT/e \doteq 10^{-2}$ volts, that is, near room temperature.

6.6 Johnson Noise

In the absence of an applied field, the generation and recombination of photoexcited carriers was seen in equation 6.12 to yield the expression for Johnson or thermal agitation noise. Since the result does not depend on the rate of excitation or the lifetime of the excited carrier, it is self evident that the result applies to thermal generation and recombination, as well, and the argument need not be repeated here.

We consider now the other extreme in which the carriers are derived from arbitrary shallow donors so that the number of carriers remains constant and there is negligible contribution to the noise currents from the processes of thermal generation and recombination. There should still, of course, be the same value of Johnson noise. The formalism of equation 6.5 can be used to derive the Johnson noise from the random displacements of the carriers in the conduction band. The number of events per second is the number of random collisions per second. The contribution per event is the fractional charge given by

$$e \frac{l}{L}$$

where l is the mean free path between collisions. Again, we are using a one-dimensional argument. Hence, the mean-squared noise current becomes

$$I_n{}^2 = 2 \frac{\mathfrak{N}}{\tau_c} \left(e \frac{l}{L} \right)^2 \Delta B \qquad (6.16)$$

We make use of the relation:

$$l = v\tau_c$$

or

$$l^2 = (v\tau_c)^2 = 2kT \frac{\mu}{e} \tau_c \qquad (6.17)$$

since $\frac{1}{2}mv^2 = \frac{1}{2}kT$ and $\tau_c e/m = \mu$. Insertion of equation 6.17 into equation 6.16 gives

$$I_n{}^2 = 4\,\frac{\mathfrak{N}e\mu}{L^2}\,kT\Delta B$$

$$= 4\,\frac{kT}{R}\,\Delta B \tag{6.18}$$

as expected.

The mean-squared noise current per unit bandwidth in any actual resistor in thermal equilibrium is, of course, a constant and given by $4kT/R$. The arguments used by Nyquist to arrive at this result are quite general and independent of mechanism. It may therefore appear artificial to single out and show how two particular mechanisms like generation–recombination and random collisions each lead to the Nyquist result. The reason for doing so is to show that under an applied field the noise currents from the two mechanisms increase at different rates. In particular, at the field kT/eL_D, the generation–recombination noise becomes significantly larger than the Nyquist value. Meantime, the noise from random collisions remains close to the Nyquist value and would be expected to depart significantly only at a field of kT/el, which is also the onset of significant heating of the electrons by the applied field.

6.7 Current Noise in Semiconductors with Traps

Again, as in the case of the photoconductor, there is a critical field at which the so-called current noise exceeds the Johnson noise. This field is

$$\mathcal{E} = \frac{kT}{eL_D}$$

where L_D, the diffusion length of a thermally excited carrier, is derived from the lifetime of a thermally excited carrier in the same way as for a photo excited carrier. The current noise is (as in eq. 6.8):

$$I_n{}^2 = 4eIG\Delta B \tag{6.19}$$

where $G = \mathcal{E}\mu\tau/L$. This argument assumes that the density of free electrons is less than the density of electrons in traps out of which the free electrons are thermally generated.

In the case for which the free carrier density *exceeds* the density of electrons in traps, the point of view for computing the noise current must be shifted to regard the free carriers as the reservoir out of which the electrons in traps are generated. In general, if one has electrons in two sets of states in thermal equilibrium, the set of states having the larger density of electrons is the "reservoir" out of which the smaller density is "generated." This point of view insures that statistical fluctuations in the rate of generation do not react back on the size of the reservoir giving a kind of negative feedback or correlation effect which would attenuate the normal statistical fluctuations. Another way of regarding this problem is to say that the two sets of states constitute a single system. The lifetimes of an electron in each set of states define two response times. The system as a whole reacts or relaxes at a rate given by the shorter lifetime, i.e., faster response time. The shorter time is associated (see eq. 6.21) with the set of states having the lower density of electrons.

We compute the noise current in terms of the rate at which electrons are fed from the free carriers into traps. By equation 6.5:

$$I_n{}^2 = 4F\alpha^2\Delta B$$

$$= 4\,\frac{n_0 L}{\tau}\left(\frac{\mathcal{E}\mu\tau_s}{L}e\right)^2\Delta B \qquad (6.20)$$

$$= 4eIG\left(\frac{\tau_s}{\tau}\right)^2\Delta B$$

Here n_0 is the density of free carriers, τ is the time an electron spends in the conduction band between trapping events and τ_s is the time an electron spends immobilized or stationary in a trap. The contribution per event is the charge *deficit*

$$\frac{\mathcal{E}\mu\tau_s}{L}e$$

incurred while the electron is residing in a trap. The fact that this is a deficit rather than an addition to the measured flow of charge in the external circuit, of course, does not affect the magnitude of the noise current. Equation 6.20 is written in a form using $G = (\mathcal{E}\mu\tau)/L$ as in equation 6.19 in order to make the two equations easy to compare. From equation 6.20, the mean squared noise current per unit bandwidth is reduced by the factor $(\tau_s/\tau)^2$ compared with equation 6.19. The total noise, however, is reduced by the factor τ_s/τ since the maximum bandwidth in equation 6.19 is

$$\Delta B = \frac{1}{2\tau}$$

and in equation 6.20 is

$$B = \frac{1}{2\tau_s}$$

Finally, by detailed balancing

$$\frac{n_0}{\tau} = \frac{n_s}{\tau_s} \tag{6.21}$$

where n_s is the density of electrons in traps. From equation 6.21:

$$\frac{\tau_s}{\tau} = \frac{n_s}{n_0} \tag{6.22}$$

and we can write equation 6.20 as

$$I_n^2 = 4eIG \left(\frac{n_s}{n_0}\right)^2 \Delta B \tag{6.23}$$

for $n_s < n_0$. For $n_s > n_0$, this factor becomes unity and we have equation 6.19.

6.8 Space-Charge-Limited Currents

One can look upon the noise component of a space-charge-limited current in two ways. One approach is to compare these currents with currents in a vacuum diode and say that the resultant noise current is a space-charge-suppressed shot noise—the virtual cathode doing the suppression. This appears to the writer to be a circuitous approach because an ordinary resistor also must have a virtual cathode to display Ohm's law. Since one does not regard the noise in an ordinary resistor as space charge-suppressed shot noise, one need not for self consistency do so for space charge-limited currents. A more direct approach is to identify a sample in which space charge-limited flow occurs with a resistor of the same value and, to a good approximation, to expect the same noise currents, including the onset of current noise at fields $\varepsilon > kT/eL_D$, as pointed out in Section 6.6.

6.9 Photoconductor-Including Traps

We consider a rate of excitation, F/sec, of electrons into the conduction band. Most of the electrons settle into traps, leaving a fraction, θ, free. We assume also that the electron is trapped in a time short compared with its lifetime. We can picture a stream of excited electrons dividing between two categories, a small fraction going to the free states and a large fraction to trapping states. This picture suggests that the noise properties might be treated in the same fashion as one would treat the noise of a stream of electrons dividing between two adjacent collecting electrodes. In this case the noise currents (neglecting space-charge effects) are computed independently for each collector in terms of the shot noise appropriate to its fraction of the current. Such a procedure, however, is highly inappropriate for the present problem. The procedure assumes that the currents arriving at the two collectors are independent. In the present problem there is a strong coupling between the trapped and free carriers via thermal excitation from and recombination into traps. To treat the two currents independently would greatly overestimate the noisiness of the free carriers.

A better approximation is to compute the noise currents as if all the carriers were excited into traps and each trapped carrier during its lifetime contributed a charge

$$\frac{\theta \mathcal{E} \mu \tau_0}{L} e \qquad (6.24)$$

to the external circuit. The time τ_0 is the lifetime of a *trapped* carrier before it returns to its recombination center. It is also the response time of the photoconductor to varying light signals. During the lifetime of a trapped carrier, it (the carrier) spends a small fraction of the time $[\theta \tau_0 = \tau = $ lifetime of a free carrier] in the conduction band. Hence the contribution per event (eq. 6.24) becomes

$$\frac{\mathcal{E} \mu \tau}{L} e \qquad (6.25)$$

But expression 6.25 is just Ge, where G is the normal photoconductive gain.

We can now write the mean-squared noise current as

$$I_n{}^2 = 4F(Ge)^2 \Delta B$$
$$= 4eIG\Delta B \qquad (6.26)$$

where I is the photoconductive current. Equation 6.26 is identical with equation 6.8, the mean-squared noise current in a trap-free photoconductor. The difference is that in equation 6.26, $\Delta B = 1/2\tau_0$, while in equation 6.8, $\Delta B = 1/2\tau$. The effect of traps has been to reduce the bandwidth of the system from that appropriate to the lifetime of a free carrier to that appropriate to the lifetime of a trapped carrier—the latter being the normal response time of the photoconductor in the presence of traps. The noise currents have been reduced by traps in the same way as they would be by the introduction of a low-pass filter in the measuring circuit. The low-frequency mean-squared noise per unit bandwidth remains substantially unchanged by the introduction of traps (see Fig. 6.3).

For frequencies greater than $B = 1/2\tau_0$, there is a small contribution to the noise spectrum from the random thermal ex-

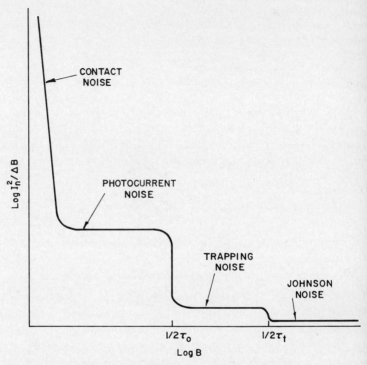

Fig. 6.3. Sources of noise in a photoconductor. Relative magnitudes are qualitative.

change traffic between the free and trapped carriers. If the lifetime of a free carrier between trapping events is $\tau_t \ll \tau$, the contribution per event (thermal excitation) is

$$e \frac{\mathscr{E}\mu\tau_t}{L} = G_t e \qquad (6.27)$$

and the corresponding mean-squared noise current (by the formalism of equation 6.5) is

$$I_n{}^2 = 4eIG_t\Delta B \qquad (6.28)$$

Here $G_t \ll G$, since $\tau_t \ll \tau$, and $\Delta B = 1/2\tau_t$.

6.10 Comparison of Noise Limitations for Photoconductors and Optical Masers

Since both photoconductors and optical masers are detectors*
and amplifiers for input radiation, it is appropriate to compare
their input noise limitations for normal (i.e., incoherent) light.

In the case of a photoconductor (or photoemitter) the smallest
detectable signal must compete with the noise current of the
incident, ambient photons at the temperature of the ambient.
This photon stream is the blackbody radiation:

$$\frac{\Delta \nu}{\lambda^2} \frac{1}{\exp{(h\nu/kT)} - 1} \qquad \text{photons cm}^{-2} \text{ sec}^{-1} \text{ steradian}^{-1}$$

or

$$\frac{\Delta \nu}{\lambda^2} \exp\left(\frac{-h\nu}{kT}\right) \qquad \text{for } h\nu > kT \qquad (6.29)$$

Usually, by operating at low temperatures, the ambient photon
stream and its attendant noise can be made negligible.

The optical maser operates by induced emission in contrast
to photoexcitation in the photoconductor, and responds not
only to the ambient photon stream noted above but also to the
stream of zero-point photons. The total stream of photons that
a signal must compete with in the optical maser is then:

$$\frac{\Delta \nu}{\lambda^2}\left(1 + \frac{1}{\exp\left(\dfrac{h\nu}{kT}\right) - 1}\right) \qquad \text{photons cm}^{-2} \text{ sec}^{-1} \text{ steradian}^{-1}$$

or

$$\frac{\Delta \nu}{\lambda^2} \qquad \text{for } h\nu > kT \qquad (6.30)$$

---

* The optical maser "detects" the presence of input radiation but does
not act as a "detector" in the technical sense of converting a signal-modu-
lated RF into a signal frequency.

In the visible spectrum and for $\Delta\nu = 10^{12}$, this stream is larger than 10^{20} photons cm^{-2} sec^{-1} sr^{-1}. It corresponds to an incident light intensity of about 10^7 foot candles per steradian! Only by restricting the acceptance angle and $\Delta\nu$ to such small values that might be derived from the output radiation of another optical maser can the ambient zero-point radiation be reduced to reasonable levels.

6.11   Comparative Noise Power in the Radio and Optical Spectra

It is useful to compare the root-mean-squared noise power incident on a receiver in the optical and radio ranges of frequencies. We use the term "optical" for frequencies such that $h\nu > kT$ and the term "radio" for frequencies such that $h\nu < kT$.

In the optical range, the photon stream is given by equation 6.29 and, since the photons are independent and random, the mean-squared noise power of the incident photons is by equation 6.5

$$P_n{}^2 = \frac{2(h\nu)^2}{\lambda^2} \exp\left(-\frac{h\nu}{kT}\right)(\Delta\nu)^2 A\omega \qquad (6.31)$$

where A is the area of receiver, ω is the solid angle over which radiation is received, $h\nu$ is used for α, the energy contribution per event, and $\Delta\nu$ is used for ΔB. The root-mean-squared noise power is

$$P_n = \frac{2^{1/2}h\nu}{\lambda} \exp\left(-\frac{h\nu}{2kT}\right)\Delta\nu(A\omega)^{1/2} \text{ ergs } cm^{-2} sec^{-1} \quad (6.32)$$

In the radio range ($h\nu < kT$), the photons can no longer be treated as independent noninteracting events. The photon stream is dense enough that several photons arrive at times and angles sufficiently close to give rise to interference. For this reason, in the formalism of equation 6.3 the factor $\bar{n}^{1/2}$ needs to be replaced by $\bar{n}$.* Hence, equation 6.4 written for the mean-squared fluctuation in power becomes

$$P_n{}^2 = F^2\alpha^2$$

or

$$P_n = F\alpha \qquad (6.33)$$

where it is understood that only those photons will be counted that arrive within a solid angle to mutually interfere. For a receiver of area A, this solid angle is λ^2/A. The total photon stream striking the receiver per second per unit solid angle is, for $h\nu < kT$:

$$\frac{A\Delta\nu}{\lambda^2}\frac{kT}{h\nu} \qquad \text{photons sec}^{-1}\text{sr}^{-1} \qquad (6.34)$$

Using equation 6.34, we write for the stream of interfering photons:

$$F = \frac{\lambda^2}{A}\left(\frac{A\Delta\nu}{\lambda^2}\frac{kT}{h\nu}\right) = \frac{kT}{h\nu}\Delta\nu \qquad (6.35)$$

and for the rms noise power striking the receiver

$$P_n = F\alpha = Fh\nu = kT\Delta\nu \qquad (6.36)$$

Here $\Delta\nu$ is the bandwidth of the receiver and the result is the familiar expression for the noise power incident on a radio receiver. In contrast to the photon receiver in the optical range, the noise does not depend upon the area of the receiver, providing $A > \lambda^2$. The area drops out in the process of selecting out only that solid angle of incident radiation within which mutual interference can take place.

If we compare equations 6.32 and 6.36, we see that the radio

---

* This is a restatement of the Einstein relation that the mean-squared fluctuation in photon density in a Hohlraum is $\langle n^2 \rangle = \bar{n}(1 + \bar{n})$, where $\bar{n} = [\exp(h\nu/kT) - 1]^{-1}$.

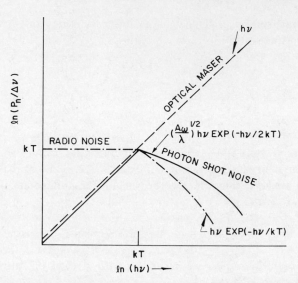

Fig. 6.4. Relative magnitudes of rms noise power per unit bandwidth of various components of Planck radiation (including zero-point radiation) incident on a receiver (or photodetector) as a function of center frequency of the receiver. $(A\omega/\lambda)^{1/2}$ is taken to be unity for convenience of representation.

noise and the optical noise power (Fig. 6.4) are comparable when $h\nu \approx kT$ if $(A\omega)^{1/2}/\lambda \approx 1$. At higher frequencies the optical noise is dominant; at lower frequencies the radio noise is dominant.

6.12   General Comments on Noise

A photoconductor is a substantially noiseless amplifier in the sense that the signal-to-noise ratio of the photoconductive current is substantially equal to the signal-to-noise ratio of the incident photon stream. To see this, we take for the signal the average current and write equation 6.6

$$\left(\frac{\text{signal}}{\text{noise}}\right)^2_{\text{in}} = \frac{F^2}{2F\Delta B} = \frac{F}{2\Delta B} \tag{6.37}$$

and from equation 6.22

$$\left(\frac{\text{signal}}{\text{noise}}\right)^2_{\text{out}} = \frac{I^2}{4eGI\Delta B} = \frac{eFG}{4eG\Delta B}$$

(6.38)

$$= \frac{F}{4\Delta B}$$

Except for a factor of 2, the two results are the same. Also, from equation 6.38 the mean-squared signal-to-noise ratio is equal numerically to half the number of incident photons in the observation time $1/2\Delta B$. This is also half the number of photo-excited electrons in the steady state in the photoconductor. The extra factor of 2 in equation 6.38 arises from statistical fluctuations of the contribution α per excited electron about its mean value. This type of departure from a noiseless amplifier is small compared with others that may arise from variations in α caused by gross inhomogeneities either in potential distribution along the sample or in lifetime of free carriers either along the sample or across the sample. The effect of these inhomogeneities is to make it look as if the output current were produced by only a fraction of the input stream of photons. Hence, by equation 6.38, the output signal-to-noise ratio is reduced. This interpretation of the effect of gross inhomogeneities is easily seen if, for example, most of the applied voltage appears across a small part of the sample such as near the cathode contact. It is clear that the output current is determined substantially only by the fraction of incident photons that strike the small fraction of photoconductor in which the voltage drop is concentrated.

A less obvious source for departures from a noiseless amplifier comes from the discussion of recombination in Section 3.15. There it was shown that under certain conditions, for two sets of recombination centers, it is as if only a fraction of the incident stream of photons is responsible for the bulk of excited carriers. The resultant photocurrent is correspondingly more noisy (lower signal-to-noise ratio) than it would be if all the photons contributed equally. It is likely that as our examination of materials becomes more sophisticated the measurement of such departures from a noiseless amplifier will become an elegant tool for getting information about defect centers in the forbidden zone.

The noise spectra we have discussed all have a constant amplitude (Fig. 6.3) along the frequency axis up to the cutoff frequency of the physical phenomenon involved. We have not discussed the common observation that towards zero frequency there is a component of noise that increases as the reciprocal of the frequency, the so-called $1/f$ noise. As the uniformity of materials and the electrical character of contacts have improved, this component of the noise spectrum has steadily decreased. There is no doubt that a poor contact, having in it an array of recombination centers with different lifetimes, can give rise to a $1/f$ type of noise. In a similar way, surface states on semiconductors which have a range of thermal escape times can generate a $1/f$ spectrum. It is not yet clear how much of the $1/f$ spectrum can be derived from volume effects in a substantially homogeneous photoconductor. Normally, a free electron averages over a variety of recombination centers to give a single average lifetime as far as noise currents are concerned. Under some conditions, however, see Section 3.15, it is as if a fraction of the free carriers "belong to" or can be identified with certain recombination centers. Under these conditions a spread in capture cross sections can give rise to a $1/f$ type spectrum.

It should be borne in mind that as one approaches zero frequency only a vanishingly small concentration of long-lived centers is needed to contribute a $1/f$ noise in excess of the normal shot noise. For example, we write the spectral density of the noise current in the form (see equation 6.8)

$$I_n{}^2/\Delta B = 4e^2FG^2$$

Let the photoexcitations, F, occur predominantly from centers for which the lifetime and gain are τ_1 and G_1, respectively. Let a small fraction, θF, of the photoexcitations be assigned to a second group of centers for which τ_2 and G_2 are much larger than τ_1 and G_1. The fraction θ needed to allow the second set of centers to dominate the low-frequency part of the noise spectrum (below $B = 1/2\tau_2$) is then

$$\theta = (G_1/G_2)^2$$

For $\tau_1 = 10^{-6}$ sec, and $\tau_2 = 1$ sec, the gains will be in the same ratio and

$$\theta = 10^{-12}$$

that is, only 10^{-12} of the radiation need be assigned to long-lived centers to cause the noise associated with their carriers to dominate the low-frequency spectrum! Since a free carrier normally averages out the two groups of centers to give a single, common lifetime, some device or mechanism is needed, such as physical separation, to decouple the two sets of centers in order to satisfy the above argument. The argument does show how sensitive the low-frequency part of the spectrum is to departures from homogeneity and does suggest that such measurements may be an exceedingly sensitive tool to test for uniformity of specimens.

References

Brophy, J. J., and R. J. Robinson, *Phys. Rev.*, 118, 959 (1960).

Petritz, R. L., *Phys. Rev.*, 104, 1508 (1956).

Rose, A., *Advances in Electronics*, Vol. I, Academic Press, New York, 1949, p. 131. Edited by L. Marton.

Rose, A., *Proc. IRE*, 43, 1850 (1955).

Shulman, C. I., *Phys. Rev.*, 98, 384 (1955).

van Vliet, K. M., *Proc. IRE*, 46, 1004 (1958).

van Vliet, K. M., J. Blok, C. Ris, and J. Steketee, *Physica*, 22, 723 (1956).

Chapter 7

Capture Cross Sections

The range of sensitivities of photoconductors is at least some twelve powers of ten and is essentially given by the range of lifetimes of free carriers. In the expression for lifetime

$$\tau = 1/n_r vs$$

the two major factors that contribute to the range of lifetimes are the recombination state density n_r and the capture cross section s for free carriers. Recombination state densities extend from about $10^{12}/cm^3$ in the more refined single crystals to close to $10^{19}/cm^3$ in the higher band gap materials where deep-lying centers can be packed more closely without overlapping wave functions. Capture cross sections range from about 10^{-12} cm^2 for Coulomb attractive capture to less than 10^{-20} cm^2 for Coulomb repulsive capture. The combination of these two ranges readily accounts for a possible range of 15 powers of ten in free-carrier lifetime or in observed photosensitivity. For a thermal velocity of 10^7 cm/sec, the lifetime of free carriers can be expected to be as long as 10 sec and as short as 10^{-14} sec. The lifetimes of sensitive photoconductors like CdS and CdSe lie in the range of 10^{-2} to 10^{-3} sec, while for insensitive photoconductors like amorphous selenium, antimony trisulfide, and sulfur, the lifetimes are 10^{-9} sec and shorter.

For the most part, capture cross sections have not been directly calculated, owing to the difficulty of getting a valid ground-state wave function for deep-lying recombination centers. The problem lies just at the transition between the tight-binding (or atomic) concepts and the effective mass (free-carrier) concept. Cross sections, as mentioned above, have been measured or estimated experimentally to be as large as 10^{-12} cm^2 for Coulomb attractive centers and as small as 10^{-20} cm^2 for centers presumed to be Coulomb repulsive.

The capture cross section has been calculated reliably only in several special cases that serve to outline part, at least, of the range of values.

7.1   Free–Free Capture

Little attention has been paid in this tract to the capture of free electrons by free holes because it is rarely the dominant or life-determining capture process. Nevertheless, the radiative recombination of free carriers is of obvious interest in luminescence even when the process is not the dominant one. Also, the calculation of the cross section for free–free radiative capture is a good measure for the cross section of other radiative capture processes into localized centers.

The argument used to compute the capture cross section makes use of detailed balance. Consider an intrinsic semiconductor in thermal equilibrium with its surround. Blackbody radiation falls on the semiconductor at the rate of

$$\frac{2\pi\nu^2}{c^2} \frac{1}{\exp{(h\nu/kT)} - 1} \Delta\nu \qquad \text{photons cm}^{-2}\text{ sec}^{-1} \qquad (7.1)$$

These photons are absorbed in a depth d in the semiconductor. For detailed balance, the same depth of semiconductor must emit an equal stream of photons. If we take $h\nu$ equal to the band gap of the semiconductor and $h\Delta\nu = kT$, the rate of emission is given by

$$n_i^2 vsd \frac{1}{2\beta^2} = \frac{2\pi\nu^2}{hc^2} \frac{kT}{\exp{(h\nu/kT)} - 1} \qquad (7.2)$$

where n_i is the density of free carriers in intrinsic material and $1/\beta^2$ is the reduced fraction of emission which escapes owing to total reflection in a medium of index of refraction β. We take $h\nu/kT > 1$ and express $n_i{}^2$ as

$$n_i{}^2 = 4\left[\frac{2\pi(m_e{}^*m_h{}^*)^{1/2}kT}{h^2}\right]^3 \exp\left(-\frac{h\nu}{kT}\right) \qquad (7.3)$$

Equation 7.2 then becomes:

$$s = \frac{h^4\beta^2 E_g{}^2}{2^{7/2}\pi^2 c^2 d m_e{}^* m_h{}^{*3/2}(kT)^{5/2}}$$

$$= 5 \times 10^{-25} \frac{\beta^2}{d} E_g{}^2 \left(\frac{m}{m^*{}_e}\right)\left(\frac{m}{m^*{}_h}\right)^{3/2}\left(\frac{300}{T}\right)^{5/2} \text{cm}^2 \qquad (7.4)$$

We have assumed $m_e{}^* < m_h{}^*$ in computing the relative thermal velocity in equation 7.2. For the inverse condition, the subscripts e and h should be interchanged in equation 7.4.

A sample evaluation of equation 7.4 gives $s = 3 \times 10^{-19}$ cm^2 for $\beta = 4$, $d = 10^{-4}$ cm, $Eg = 2$ ev, $m_e{}^* = m_h{}^* = m$, and $T = 300°$K. Values one or two powers of ten larger or smaller, respectively, can be obtained for smaller effective masses and larger values of the absorption distance d encountered in cases of indirect optical transitions at the band edge.

Radiative capture even into a localized center should also yield capture cross sections in the order of 10^{-20} cm^2. Suppose, for example, that a free carrier is to be captured into a ground state, the diameter of whose wave function is 10^{-7} cm. A thermal electron will traverse such a center in 10^{-14} sec. Since the radiation time is not likely to be smaller than 10^{-8} sec, the electron will undergo radiative capture only once in every 10^6 passes. Hence, using 10^{-14} cm^2 as the area of the ground state, the capture cross section will be 10^{-6} of this value or 10^{-20} cm^2.

It is worth noting that in the case of free–free capture, radiative lifetimes as short as 10^{-8} sec can, in principle, be achieved by taking advantage of the high carrier densities in degenerate materials. Under these conditions, free–free radiative capture should be able to compete with the usual nonradiative capture into localized centers.

7.2 Coulomb Capture

The largest value for capture cross section is readily computed by asking at what radius will a free electron diffuse into an attractive Coulomb center rather than away from it? A particle executing Brownian motion at a distance r from a point p will diffuse away from the point with an average velocity of

$$v \frac{2l}{3r} \tag{7.5}$$

where v is the thermal velocity of the particle and l its mean free path between collisions. This may readily be derived by recognizing the increased space available to a diffusing electron toward larger as opposed to smaller radial distances from p. In the actual case of an electron near a *positively* charged center, the electron is also drawn toward the center at a drift velocity

$$v_d = \mathcal{E}\mu = \frac{e}{Kr^2}\mu \tag{7.6}$$

We equate the drift and diffusion velocities of equations 7.5 and 7.6 to get

$$
\begin{aligned}
r_c &= \frac{e}{Kvl}\mu = \frac{e}{Kvl}\tau\frac{e}{m} \\
&= \frac{e^2}{Kmv^2} = \frac{e^2}{2KkT}
\end{aligned} \tag{7.7}
$$

That is, the capture radius, r_c, is that radius at which the Coulomb potential of the capturing center is $2kT/e$ down from the continuum (Fig. 7.1). For radii smaller than this, the electron is drawn rapidly into the center by the increasing Coulomb field. For radii larger than r_c, the diffusion velocity, directed away from the center, exceeds the drift velocity toward the center.

The same result as equation 7.7 can be obtained by asking what is the minimum in the probability distribution of an electron around a Coulomb center? The probability of finding an electron at a given radius r is proportional to the product

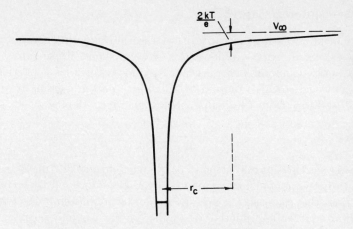

Fig. 7.1. Capture by attractive Coulomb center.

of the spherical area and the Boltzmann factor

$$\exp \frac{eV(r)}{kT}$$

where $V(r)$ is the potential measured down from the continuum
Hence,

$$P(r) \propto 4\pi r^2 \exp (eV(r)/kT) \tag{7.8}$$

$$\frac{dP(r)}{dr} \propto 8\pi r \exp (eV(r)/kT) + 4\pi r^2 \frac{e}{kT}\left(\frac{dV(r)}{dr}\right)$$

$$\exp (eV(r)/kT) = 0$$

or

$$2 + \frac{er}{kT}\left(\frac{dV(r)}{dr}\right) = 0 \tag{7.9}$$

Since $V(r) = e/Kr$ and $dV(r)/dr = -e/Kr^2$, equation 7.9 becomes

$$r = e^2/2KkT \tag{7.10}$$

in agreement with equation 7.7.

We can now write for the capture cross section,

$$s = \pi r^2 = \pi \left(\frac{e^2}{2KkT}\right)^2 \text{cm}^2 \qquad (7.11)$$

For room temperature and $K = 10$, equation 7.11 gives 2.4×10^{-13} cm^2 for the capture cross section. At $3°$K, equation 7.11 would give a capture cross section of 2.3×10^{-9} cm^2. This is to be regarded as an upper limit to the capture cross section for the following reason.

The Coulomb capture cross section computed above assumed that the electron could be regarded as a diffusing particle close to the capturing center. This means that its mean free path for energy loss should be less than the capture radius or less than about 20 A at room temperature. At $3°$K, this would be 2000 Å. If the mean free path is larger than the capture radius, equation 7.11 can still be used as a guide by multiplying it by the ratio of the diameter of the capturing center to the mean free path, lp, for loss of a phonon. This operation recognizes that the electron will pass through the center a number of times before being captured. Hence, equation 7.11 with this correction becomes

$$s = \frac{2\pi}{lp} \left(\frac{e^2}{2KkT}\right)^3 \text{cm}^2 \qquad (7.12)$$

If we take the mean free path for loss of energy to be proportional to the mobility mean free path and take $\mu \propto T^{-3/2}$, equation 7.12 gives

$$s \propto T^{-2} \qquad (7.13)$$

The data on capture by shallow Coulomb centers in germanium as summarized by Ascarelli and Rodríguez (Fig. 7.2) follow an approximate T^{-2} law in the range of 2 to $10°$K. At $6°$K the experimental cross section is 10^{-12} cm^2. If the room-temperature mobility is extrapolated to $6°$K by the $T^{-3/2}$ relation, the cross section computed from equation 7.12 is 0.3×10^{-12} cm^2 on the assumption that the mean free path for energy loss and the mobility mean free path are equal.

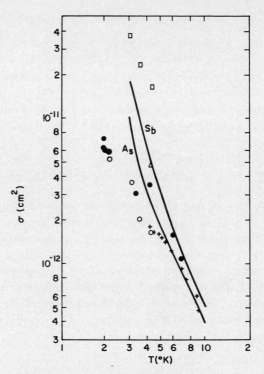

Fig. 7.2. Compilation of data on capture cross sections of shallow donors in germanium [taken from Ascarelli and Rodriguez, *Phys. Rev.*, **124**, 1325 (1961)]. The solid lines are the theoretical curves of Ascarelli and Rodriguez.

It is valid to extrapolate the lattice-controlled mobility and ignore scattering by ionized impurities, since it is only the energy exchange with the lattice phonons that allows an electron to be captured by the Coulomb center.

Ascarelli and Rodriguez have computed the capture cross section of shallow Coulomb centers by treating in detail the capture process of free electrons into the various excited levels of the hydrogenic centers and match the experimental data reasonably well (Fig. 7.2).

The validity of the simple expression for lifetime

$$\tau = 1/n_r vs \qquad (7.14)$$

requires that the mean free path be comparable with or larger than the diameter of the capturing centers and larger than some fraction of the spacing between capturing centers. The first condition insures that the effective volume traced out by the Brownian motion of the free electron has negligible overlap. The second condition insures that the point of origin of the free electron relative to the capturing centers is not critical. In the event that the mean free path is appreciably less than the spacing between capturing centers, the electrons will diffuse to the centers and show a spread in lifetimes depending on the distance of their point of origin from the nearest capturing centers. Even for the case of capture by diffusion we can approximate an expression of the form of equation 7.14.

We consider an electron starting from a point $L/2$ removed from the nearest capturing center, L being the spacing between centers. Such an electron will diffuse out to a radius $L/2$ in a time

$$eL^2/4kT\mu \qquad (7.15)$$

At this radius, the fraction of the diffusing pattern intercepted by the capturing centers is

$$\frac{ms}{4\pi(L/2)^2} \qquad (7.16)$$

where m is the number of the nearest neighbor capturing centers. Hence, the capture time will be expression 7.15 divided by expression 7.16 or

$$\tau = \frac{eL^2\pi L^2}{4kT\mu ms}$$

$$= \frac{3\pi}{4m}\frac{1}{n_r v(sl/L)} \qquad (7.17)$$

Equation 7.17 can be written in the form

$$\tau = 1/n_r vs^* \qquad (7.18)$$

where

$$s^* = s\left(\frac{4m}{3\pi}\frac{l}{L}\right) \tag{7.19}$$

If we take $m = 4$, equation 7.19 must be used for the capture cross section when $l < L/2$.

7.3   Capture by Repulsive Coulomb Centers

Free atoms can capture at most one extra electron. The second electron sees a repulsive potential even at small distances. Impurity states in a solid can capture more than one charge, partly because the Coulomb field of the first charge is largely polarized out and partly because the valence forces of surrounding atoms can play a large attractive role at close spacings. There is, for example, good evidence that gold in germanium can be a triple acceptor. Similarly, it is thought that cadmium vacancies in CdS can capture two extra electrons, making the center doubly negative. If one of these electrons is removed by light it finds difficulty in returning to the center, owing to the repulsive field at large distances. Only when it approaches sufficiently close can it "see" an attractive field. To do so, the electron must surmount a potential barrier (Fig. 7.3). Hence, the effective capture cross section for capturing a free electron

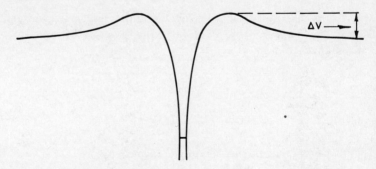

Fig. 7.3. Capture by repulsive Coulomb center.

is reduced. If, for example, the top of the potential hill occurs at a radius of 4 A, the height of the hill will be 0.37 volts in a material having a dielectric constant of 10. A reduction in cross section by the Boltzmann factor

$$\exp\left(-\frac{0.37\,e}{kT}\right)$$

would be expected, so that at room temperature the reduction factor would be 10^{-6}. This factor multiplied into a cross section of 9×10^{-15} cm^2 gives 2×10^{-21} cm^2, a value close to that observed in sensitized crystals of CdS. On the other hand, one would expect this cross section to be highly temperature dependent. The evidence for this is not altogether clear. It is true that extremely long-lived centers have been found in CdS and in nickel-doped germanium at liquid air temperature.

7.4 Macroscopic Barriers

It is relatively easy to visualize long lifetimes of free carriers arising from macroscopic barriers in crystals. Particularly, at the surface of an N-type crystal, if the bands bend "up" (see Fig. 7.4), the free pairs generated in the surface barrier would break up into a free electron going to the interior and a bound hole at the surface. The electron would have to surmount the surface barrier to recombine with the hole and, hence, could

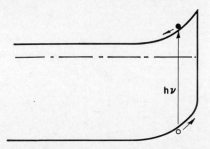

Fig. 7.4. Enhanced lifetime resulting from macroscopic barrier.

remain free for a long time. Such barriers, of course, may occur in the volume as well, particularly at grain boundaries. The analysis of the photoconductivity of thin films of lead sulfide (activated by oxidation) appears to fit this pattern.

Such barriers also reduce the surface recombination of free pairs in germanium and silicon by impeding the access of one or the other member of the free pair to the recombination states at the surface.

References

Ascarelli, G., and S. Rodriguez, *Phys. Rev.*, **124**, 1325 (1961).
Koenig, S. H., *Phys. Rev.*, **110**, 988 (1958).
Lax, M., *Phys. Rev.*, **119**, 1502 (1960).
Rose, A., *RCA Rev.*, **12**, 362 (1951).
Stöckmann, F., *Z. Physik*, **130**, 477 (1951).
Van Roosbroeck, W., and W. Shockley, *Phys. Rev.*, **94**, 1558 (1954).

Chapter 8

Electrical Contacts

8.1 Neutral Contacts

The simplest metal-semiconductor contact is that shown in Fig. 8.1a. The conduction band remains flat out to the metal interface. The contact is called neutral in contrast to those contacts in which the bands bend up or down at the interface. The maximum current that can be drawn from a neutral contact is the thermionic emission from the metal over the potential step into the semiconductor. The maximum thermionic emission is, by detailed balance, equal to the random current from semiconductor to metal. Hence, the thermionic emission will be saturated at an electric field in the semiconductor given by

$$\frac{n_0 e v}{4} = \mathcal{E} n_0 e \mu \tag{8.1}$$

or

$$\mathcal{E} = v/4\mu \text{ volts/cm} \tag{8.2}$$

For a mobility of 10^2 cm^2/volt-sec and a thermal velocity of 10^7 cm/sec, equation 8.2 gives a saturating field of 2.5×10^4 volts/cm. At this field, departures from Ohm's law begin to occur also because the carriers become heated by the field and their mobility changes.

For fields less than the saturating value given in equation 8.2, the current drawn through the semiconductor is less than that "available" from the metal and the contact is "Ohmic." It is Ohmic in the sense that an increase in field in the semi-

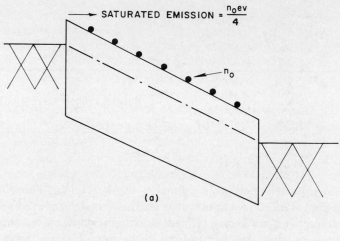

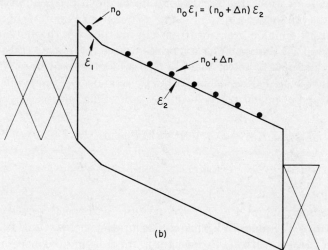

Fig. 8.1. Neutral contact. (a) Volume unilluminated. (b) Volume
illuminated.

conductor will give a proportional increase in current. It is
Ohmic in the sense, also, that the contact can supply the additional current needed when the semiconductor is made more

conducting by light. In the latter case, the effect of the added carriers, Δn, is to steepen the electric field at the contact in order to supply the additional current (Fig. 8.1b). The range of photocurrents for which the contact is Ohmic is, of course, limited to values less than the saturated thermionic emission. For light intensities higher than those needed to saturate the thermionic emission, the contact is "blocking," that is, it supplies no additional carriers to replace those excited by the light in the volume of the semiconductor and drawn out at the anode. At these higher light intensities, the field becomes more and more concentrated near the electrode where the carriers enter.

While a neutral contact is defined as one in which the bands remain flat out to the contact, it is clear that a mild curvature of the bands in the blocking direction will also act like a neutral contact for a more limited range of fields. Equation 8.1 can be rewritten for this case:

$$\frac{ven}{4} \exp\left(-\frac{e\Delta V}{kT}\right) = \mathcal{E}ne\mu \qquad (8.3)$$

or

$$\mathcal{E} = \frac{v}{4\mu} \exp\left(-\frac{e\Delta V}{kT}\right) \text{volts/cm} \qquad (8.4)$$

ΔV is the departure from the flat band condition. Equation 8.4 shows that the emission from the contact is rapidly saturated at lower fields as ΔV increases. For values of ΔV such that the field in equation 8.4 is

$$\mathcal{E} < kT/eL$$

where L is the sample length, the contact acts like a simple diode rectifier in which the back current is saturated with an applied voltage of a few kT/e.

8.2 Blocking Contacts

As noted in the previous section, a blocking contact (Fig. 8.2) is one whose emission current is saturated. Increasing the

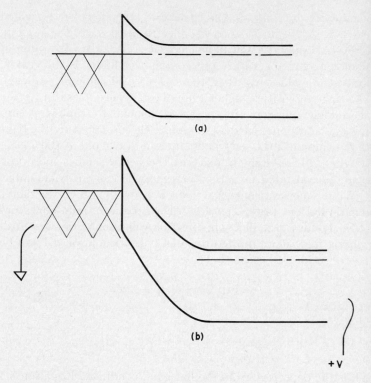

Fig. 8.2. Blocking contact. (a) Zero applied voltage. (b) Finite applied voltage.

electric field near the contact, or increasing the conductivity of the semiconductor, does not lead to an increase in current from the contact. A temperature-limited vacuum diode and a vacuum photocell are familiar examples where the cathode acts as a blocking contact to vacuum. Similarly, metal–semiconductor rectifiers and P-N junctions biased in the back direction are familiar examples of blocking contacts in solids.

The earlier discussion of photoconductivity in this tract has assumed the presence of "Ohmic" as opposed to blocking contacts. The photo properties using blocking contacts are not governed by the gain–bandwidth product derived in Chapter 5. The photo properties are, in fact, quite simple. If only one sign of carrier is photoexcited in the volume of the photoconductor no steady photocurrents can be drawn. If one sign of carrier is excited at the contact or if both signs of carrier are excited in the volume, a steady photocurrent equal to the rate of photo-excitation can be drawn through the sample. That is, the photoconductive gain is unity and cannot (in the absence of impact ionization) exceed unity. The response time is equal to the drift transit time of carriers through the sample and can be made as small as the saturated drift velocity of carriers will permit. The latter is in the neighborhood of 10^7 cm/sec.

Two well-documented examples of blocking contacts are the photocurrents in amorphous selenium as used in Xerography, an electrophotographic process, and the photocurrents in thin layers of zinc oxide powder as used in Electrofax, also an electrophotographic process. In both cases, the photoexcitations are generated by strongly absorbed light at a blocking contact and the highest photoconductive gain is unity. Response times in Electrofax have been observed [Gerritsen et al.] to be in the order of seconds and have been identified with the trap-dominated drift transit time of electrons through the thin layer of zinc oxide. The transit time of free carriers in the same samples should be in the order of 10^{-9} sec. At low voltages, the gain is less than unity and is in some cases, proportional to the applied voltage. In this range, it is likely that the photoexcited carriers recombine before being drawn through the sample. An exaggerated example of the predominant role of recombination was shown by Weimer for strongly absorbed, high-intensity illumination of amorphous selenium operated at low voltages. The photocurrent did not increase with increasing light intensity. A high density or reservoir of free holes was generated at the anode and acted as a virtual Ohmic contact to the rest of the material. The result was a space charge-limited current that depended on the applied voltage but not on the light intensity.

Adjacent to a blocking contact is an exhaustion layer in the semiconductor (see Fig. 8.2). The width of this layer can be computed by a simple condenser relation in which the separation of plates is taken to be half the exhaustion layer thickness owing to the distributed nature of the charge. Thus:

$$Q = CV$$

$$neL = \frac{KV}{2\pi L} \times 10^{-12}$$

$$L = \left(\frac{KV}{2\pi ne}\right)^{1/2} \times 10^{-6} \text{ cm}$$

$$= \left(\frac{KV}{2\pi n}\right)^{1/2} \times 2.5 \times 10^{3} \text{ cm} \tag{8.5}$$

where V is the sum of the applied voltage and the contact potential (departure from flat band) and n is the density of available charge in the semiconductor. In problems involving germanium and silicon crystals, n is often taken as the free-carrier density. This is valid if the free-carrier density exceeds the density of electrons (or holes) in traps. In general, for relatively insulating materials, n is the sum of free and trapped electrons and is usually dominated by the latter. The term "available" is used to describe those trapped electrons that can be thermally evacuated in the time of the experiment. Obviously, electrons trapped deeper than an electron volt can take unrealistically long times to be thermally excited to the conduction band at room temperature. Since the density of trapped electrons is in the order of $10^{15}/\text{cm}^3$, the depletion layer thickness is likely to be only microns thick even for insulating materials where the free-carrier density is vanishingly small

8.3 Ohmic Contacts

An Ohmic contact is one that supplies a reservoir of carriers freely available to enter the semiconductor as needed. This may seem like a circuitous way of describing a contact in which

the bands bend in such a way as to increase the density of
carriers at the contact relative to the volume of the semiconductor. The definition, however, includes also the case described
in Section 8.2, where strongly absorbed, high-itensity illumination can provide an Ohmic contact even in the absence of a
"bending of the bands." Also, blocking contacts that are thin
enough to permit tunneling of carriers from metal to semiconductor act like Ohmic contacts insofar as Ohm's law is
readily observed, and space charge currents should be observable. In this case, only a negligible voltage is needed across the
depletion layer to provide the necessary tunneling current and
the contacts can be regarded as "quasi-Ohmic." Finally, a
neutral contact acts like an Ohmic contact in the narrow sense
of yielding Ohm's law within the range of its saturated emission.
A neutral contact does not have a reservoir of carrier density
exceeding the bulk density of carriers and hence cannot yield
space charge-limited currents.

Figure 8.3 shows an Ohmic contact obtained by the combination of metal and semiconductor for which the metal has the
lower work function. The solution given by Mott and Gurney
for the distribution of potential in the semiconductor starting
from the surface is

$$V = 2V_t \ln\left(\frac{x}{L_1} + 1\right) \text{ volts} \tag{8.6}$$

where

$$L_1 = \left(\frac{KV_t}{2\pi n_1}\right)^{1/2} \times 2.5 \times 10^3 \text{ cm}; \quad V_t \equiv kT/e \tag{8.7}$$

and for the charge density

$$\rho = \frac{en_1}{\left(\dfrac{x}{L_1} + 1\right)^2} \tag{8.8}$$

where n_1 is the density of carriers at the surface and is large
compared with the thermal equilibrium density n_0 of carriers

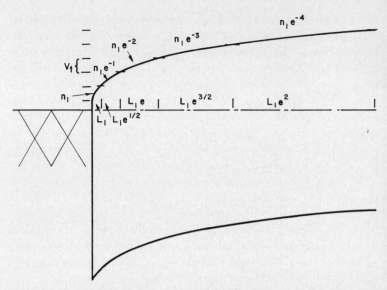

Fig. 8.3. Density of electrons and rise in potential near an Ohmic contact. L_1 is the Debye length for the density n_1.

in the bulk of the semiconductor, and x is distance measured from the surface. L_1 is readily recognized as $\sqrt{2} \times$ Debye length. (The Debye length has the same form as the depletion layer thickness (eq. 8.5) with V replaced by $kT/2e$.) For this reason, Figure 8.3 has been plotted as a series of "Debye" lengths* where each successive "Debye" length exceeds the previous one by the square root of the Naperian base e. The potential changes by V_t for each "Debye" length according to equation 8.6. (For the first few "Debye" lengths, this is an approximation.) Finally, the charge density decreases as the square of the Naperian base for each successive "Debye" length.

Three features of this charge distribution are particularly noteworthy and will be made use of below. First, half the total

---

* The notation "Debye" is a reminder that the lengths used here exceed the normal definition of a Debye length by the factor $\sqrt{2}$.

charge lies in the first "Debye" length. Second, almost half the total width of the charge layer lies in the last "Debye" length. Third, the total potential change up to the mth "Debye" length is

$$\Delta V = mV_t$$

$$= kT/e \ln (n_m/n_1) \tag{8.9}$$

We compute now the volume density of induced charge at the surface of a semiconductor resulting from an applied voltage V between metal and semiconductor when they are separated by a spacing d. For metal–semiconductor spacings d large compared with a Debye length in the semiconductor, the surface charge in the semiconductor is given by the condenser relation

$$\sigma = CV$$

$$= \frac{V}{4\pi d} \times 10^{-12} \text{ coul/cm}^2 \tag{8.10}$$

This surface charge lies in the first Debye length within the surface as long as

$$\sigma \leq n_0 e L_0 \tag{8.11}$$

Here, L_0 is the "Debye" length computed for the thermal equilibrium density n_0 of carriers in the semiconductor.

At closer spacings between metal and semiconductor it will be true that

$$\sigma \gg n_0 e L_0 \tag{8.12}$$

Under these conditions the charge is distributed over a series of "Debye" lengths such that the shortest "Debye" length is at the surface and contains half the total charge. Hence we can write:

$$\sigma \doteq \frac{V}{4\pi d} \times 10^{-12} = n_1 e L_1 \tag{8.13}$$

where n_1 is the field-enhanced density of carriers in the first

"Debye" length and $n_1 \gg n_0$, the density of thermal equilibrium carriers. Equation 8.13 is an approximation because we have neglected the part of the potential drop that occurs within the semiconductor. By equation 8.9 this correction is

$$\Delta V = kT/e \ln (n_1/n_0) \qquad (8.14)$$

The first "Debye" length is

$$L_1 = \left(\frac{KV_t}{2\pi n_1}\right)^{1/2} \times 2.5 \times 10^3 \text{ cm} \qquad (8.15)$$

Combination of equations 8.13 and 8.15 yields

$$n_1 = 2.5 \times 10^5 \left(\frac{V}{d}\right)^2 \frac{1}{KV_t} /\text{cm}^3 \qquad (8.16)$$

and

$$L_1 = 2Kd \frac{V_t}{V} \text{ cm} \qquad (8.17)$$

Note that the charge layer by equation 8.17 becomes compressed closer to the surface at the higher fields.

Equation 8.17 also shows the continuity of flux across the vacuum–semiconductor boundary, namely,

$$\mathcal{E}_{\text{vacuum}} = K \mathcal{E}_{\text{semicon}}$$

or (compare eq. 8.6 for $\mathcal{E}_{\text{semicon}}$)

$$\frac{V}{d} = K \left(2 \frac{V_t}{L_1}\right) \qquad (8.18)$$

From equation 8.16 we can compute the electric field needed to make the semiconductor degenerate at the surface. We set n_1 equal to $10^{19}/\text{cm}^3$ and $K = 10$ and obtain an electric field of 3×10^6 volts/cm.

Figure 8.4 shows the approach, in the absence of an applied field, of a metal of low work function to a semiconductor to form an Ohmic contact. In the light of the preceding discussion the successive stages are easily understood. We assume that

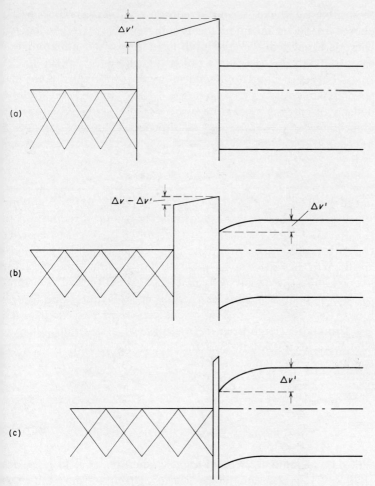

Fig. 8.4. Reduction of contact potential as metal approaches semiconductor.

the work functions of metal and semiconductor do not change
as they approach contact and that there is a negligible density
of surface states.

In Figure 8.4a, the metal and semiconductor are sufficiently separated by the criterion of equation 8.11 that the surface charge in the semiconductor lies in the first Debye length; there is a negligible potential drop in the semiconductor; and essentially all of the contact potential difference ΔV lies in the space between metal and semiconductor. In Figure 8.4b, the spacing is reduced so that equation 8.12 is satisfied; the volume density of carriers, n_1, at the surface of the semiconductor now greatly exceeds the thermal equilibrium value n_0; there is a depression of the conduction band

$$\Delta V' = kT/e \ln (n_1/n_0) \tag{8.19}$$

in the semiconductor; and the contact potential difference in the space between metal and semiconductor has been reduced from ΔV to $\Delta V - \Delta V'$. Finally, at contact (Fig. 8.4c), essentially the entire contact potential lies in the semiconductor; the potential drop in the lattice spacing between metal and semiconductor is negligible; the density of carriers at the surface of the semiconductor is higher than its thermal equilibrium value by the factor $\exp (\Delta V/kT)$; and electrons can tunnel freely through the thin potential barrier between metal and semiconductor. The field in the lattice spacing separating metal from semiconductor is, by equation 8.18,

$$\mathcal{E}_{\text{vacuum}} = 2K \frac{V_t}{L_1} \tag{8.20}$$

$$= 0.8 \ (K V_t 2\pi n_1)^{1/2} \times 10^{-3} \text{ volts/cm}$$

Since the example shown is nondegenerate, this field is less than 3×10^6 volts/cm and the potential drop less than 0.1 volts.

We have neglected the effect of surface states in screening the interior of the semiconductor from the field between metal and semiconductor. This is a justified approximation if the density of surface states near the Fermi level is less than $10^{12}/\text{cm}^2$. Such surface-state densities can support fields of less than 10^6 volts/ cm. On the other hand, surface-state densities of $10^{13}/\text{cm}^2$ and larger can absorb most of the contact potential difference in the last lattice spacing between metal and semiconductor and hence shield the interior of the semiconductor.

We have now the basis for exploring the effects of an applied field within the semiconductor on the charge and potential distribution at the contact. Consider first (Fig. 8.5) an applied field E_{a1} whose magnitude is less than the electric field in the last Debye length. The potential barrier is lowered on sudden application of the field by less than V_t and the contact supplies by diffusion just the current needed by the semiconductor without any significant transient. The reason for this is that the carrier density at the virtual cathode (energy maximum),

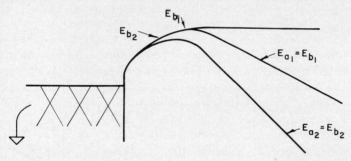

Fig. 8.5. Potential distribution near an Ohmic contact for two applied fields.

where the applied field cancels the electric field in the last Debye length, is closely the same as in the semiconductor. Further, before the semiconductor field was applied there was a balance between diffusion and electric field currents in the charge layer. The cancellation of the electric field in the charge layer by the applied field occurs, of course, where the two fields have equal and opposite magnitudes and where the effective diffusion field is numerically equal to the applied field. Hence, at the virtual cathode, the product of diffusion field and carrier density is closely the same as the product of electric field and carrier density in the body of the semiconductor.

By way of contrast, let the applied field in the semiconductor, E_{a2}, be some 100-fold larger than that in the last Debye length. At $t = 0$, when the field in the semiconductor is first applied, it will cancel the electric field in the charge layer at a point several Debye lengths removed from the last Debye length. From Figure 8.3, this will be eight Debye lengths removed from the end. Also from Figure 8.3, the electron density will be e^8 or more than 10^3 times the density in the bulk of the semi-conductor. As before, the diffusion field will be equal to the applied field. The net result is that the contact will begin to supply current to the semiconductor at a level more than 10^3 times larger than the current in the semiconductor. The virtual cathode, which started out at eight Debye lengths removed from the end, will be reestablished at some intermediate value such that the product of diffusion field and carrier density will supply just the current needed by the semiconductor.

The above discussion is needed to understand the conditions for observing the large transient space-charge-limited currents reported by Smith under pulsed voltages applied to CdS crystals. Van Heerden discusses this problem also for transient space-charge currents in germanium. In both cases, the applied field was larger than the field in the last Debye length and sufficiently large to uncover the higher density of carriers at the contact needed to support the large pulsed, space-charge-limited currents. The pulse form of the space-charge-limited current comes about because the initial space-charge-limited current is that appropriate to a trap-free crystal. As the free carriers become trapped, the initial large current decays to a relatively low steady-state value appropriate to a crystal with traps.

The discussion also clarifies the possible contribution of the contact to the response time of a photoconductor. Suppose that the current in a photoconductor is to be doubled by doubling the light intensity while keeping the applied field constant. The current supplied by the contact must also be doubled. To do so, a positive charge must be built up in the volume of the photoconductor sufficient to lower the virtual cathode by about V_t. Quantitatively, this means the number of positive charges formed in the photoconductor must be equal to the number of available charges in the Debye length at the virtual cathode. (See reference by Lampert and Rose.) This contribution to response time will be significant when the number of available electron charges in a Debye length at the virtual cathode exceed the total number of free and trapped charges in thermal contact with the conduction band in the volume of the photoconductor. This can occur since at the contact the recombination centers also contribute to the available charge, while in the bulk only the traps contribute. The latter normally determine the response time of the photoconductor.

8.4 Metal–Semiconductor Contacts

The simplest guide to choosing an Ohmic or blocking contact is the well-known criterion of picking a metal with a work function smaller or larger, respectively, than the semiconductor. This is only a rough guide and one that often fails for elementary reasons of which screening by surface states is perhaps the most common. The criterion would be valid if the work functions of metal and semiconductor did not change on contact. Actually, dipole layers on the two surfaces contribute part of the work functions and interact on contact in as yet unpredictable ways. An obvious source of uncertainty is shown in Figure 8.6. Here we have a metal and semiconductor with the same work function. If we add a monolayer of cesium to the metal we get a lower work function and expect an Ohmic contact. If, instead, we add the monolayer of cesium to the semiconductor, we would expect a blocking contact. All of this is based on the contact potential difference between metal and semiconductor before contact. After contact, the cesium does not know on which surface it was first deposited and hence arrives at the same final state independent of which surface it started on. The final state probably depends more on the intimate chemistry of valence bonds than on simple physical concepts.

Another source of ambiguity is the following. We know, for example, that the electron levels of certain impurities like

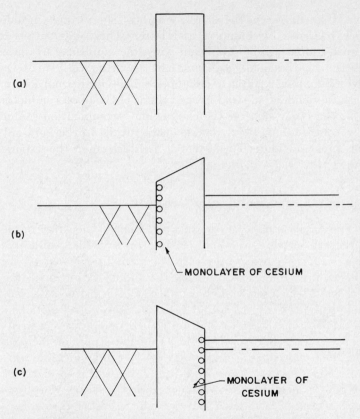

Fig. 8.6. Ambiguity of surface dipole layers for contact behavior.

indium incorporated substitutionally in germanium lie close to the valence band. Yet if indium were incorporated interstitially, there is reason to believe that its energy levels should be close to the conduction band. In any event, the work function of indium is less than the electron affinity of germanium, and hence indium on germanium should tend to make contact to the conduction band. But in an actual contact of indium with germanium, one can believe that, owing to the atomic roughness of the surface (Fig. 8.7), some indium atoms would feel them-

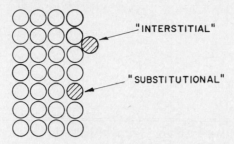

Fig. 8.7. Ambiguity between "interstitial" and "substitutional" sites of foreign atoms on a surface.

selves to be in substitutional sites and others in interstitial sites. The same indium contact could then be Ohmic to both the conduction and valence bands.*

In the case of indium or gallium on CdS, the problem is less ambiguous since these materials should make Ohmic contact to the conduction band both by the work function argument and by the valence argument when indium and gallium are considered as substitutional impurities in CdS. In practice, they both act reliably as Ohmic contacts to the conduction band.

8.5 Electrolyte–Semiconductor Contacts

The use of an electrolyte to contact a semiconductor yields one of the most effective blocking contacts, for reasons that are evident from Figure 8.8. Here the electrolyte is used to contact the negative end of an N-type semiconductor. The electrons in the electrolytic contact are on the negative ions in the electrolyte and are likely to be located energetically even below the upper edge of the valence band in the semiconductor (see Fig. 9.3). Hence they have more difficulty entering the conduction

---

* W. Mehl (private communication) has succeeded in plating gold on freshly cleaved, oxide-free germanium. The surface had many steps in it. The plated gold made good contact to both N-type and P-type material.

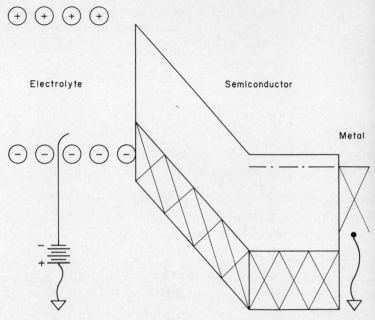

Fig. 8.8. Electrolyte-semiconductor contact with applied voltage in blocking direction.

band than the valence electrons. One consequence of this is that under applied fields large enough to cause tunneling, the tunneling is likely to occur from the valence band (Zener emission) before it occurs from the electrode (field emission). In the case of a metal contact the reverse is true, since the metal electrons usually lie energetically above the valence band.

8.6   Metal–Electrolyte Contacts

It is instructive to look briefly at a metal–electrolyte contact (Fig. 8.9) in comparison with a metal–semiconductor contact. The striking difference is that in the range of voltages up to about a volt for which the metal–electrolyte contact can be "blocking," it shows an extremely high capacitance correspond-

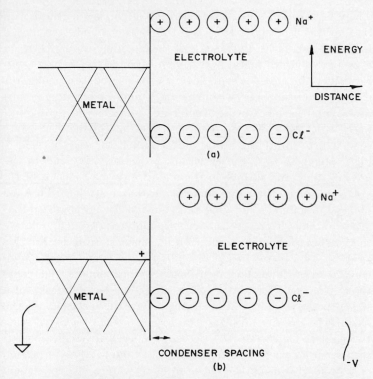

Fig. 8.9. Metal–electrolyte contact showing source of high capacitance.
(a) Zero applied voltage. (b) Applied voltage (electrolyte negative).

ing to a spacing of "plates" of only about an angstrom. This
means that the contact is supporting a field of 10^8 volts/cm,
in contrast to maximum fields $\approx 10^6$ volts/cm in solids. The
reason the metal–electrolyte can support such high fields is that
the conduction in the electrolyte is by the actual ions themselves
rather than electrons. When the metal electrode is biased positively, the negative ions of the electrolyte approach within an
angstrom of the plate. The electrons on the negative ions lie
energetically a few volts below the Fermi level in the metal and
hence cannot flow into the metal either directly or by tunneling.

There is, in brief, a negligible density of carriers at the Fermi level in the electrolyte. It is as if the valence band itself moves to carry the current. In the case of the blocking contact between a positive charged metal and a high-conductivity p-type *semiconductor*, the metal Fermi level is so located that holes (or electron) can tunnel between the metal and semiconductor thus destroying the blocking character at electric fields small compared with 10^8 volts/cm. The negative ions in the electrolyte tend to pile up at the metal surface until the electric field is high enough to raise the electrons on the negative ions to the level of the Fermi surface in the metal. This means fields of 10^8 volts/cm, or of the same magnitude that exist between ionic planes in an ionic solid. One can think of the energy-level diagram for the electrolyte as actually sliding (Fig. 8.9) relative to that for the metal at the contact surface. In order for this to occur at a metal–insulator contact, one would need a high concentration of mobile positively charged donors and negatively charged acceptors. This is, of course, the definition of a solid electrolyte. In general, even before the electrons on the electrolyte ions are raised to the Fermi surface, chemical reactions set in to provide the necessary energy to facilitate their transfer from electrolyte to metal. An example is the formation of O_2 and H_2 during the electrolysis of water. The conversion of the energy, released when O_2 is formed, to the raising of an electron from OH^- to the Fermi level of the metal electrode must be an involved process.

Much of the difference between the physics and chemistry of metal–electrolyte contacts can be epitomized by comparing the current flow between a metal and ice on the one hand, and a metal and water on the other. Assuming the flow of charges between metal and ice to be confined to electronic processes only, that between metal and water can be distinguished from it by having the added complication or degrees of freedom of chemical reactions and the mobility of the "valence band" (OH^- ions) and "conduction band" (H^+ ions) as a whole.

References

Amick, J. A., *RCA Rev.*, **20**, 770 (1959).

Bardeen, J., *Phys. Rev.*, **71**, 717 (1947).

Gerritsen, H. J., W. Ruppel, and A. Rose, *Helv. Phys. Acta*, **30**, 504 (1957).

Lampert, M. A., and A. Rose, *Phys. Rev.*, **113**, 1236 (1959).

Macdonald, J. Ross, *Solid-State Electron.*, **5**, 11 (1962).

Mott, N. F., and R. W. Gurney, *Electronic Processes in Ionic Crystals*, Oxford University Press, New York, 1940.

Ruppel, W., *Photoconductivity*, 1962, Pergamon Press, London, p. 199. Edited by H. Levinstein.

Smith, R. W., *Phys. Rev.*, **97**, 1525 (1955).

Stöckmann, F., *Halbleiterprobleme*, **6**, 279 (1961).

Van Heerden, P. J., *Phys. Rev.*, **108**, 230 (1957).

Weimer, P. K., and A. D. Cope, *RCA Rev.*, **12**, 314 (1951).

Williams, R., *Phys. Rev.*, **117**, 1487 (1960).

Williams, R., *J. Chem. Phys.*, **32**, 1505 (1960).

Williams, R., and R. H. Bube, *J. Appl. Phys.*, **31**, 968 (1960).

Chapter 9

Energy Levels in Solids and Electrolytes

The computation of the electron energy levels and ground-state wave functions of deep-lying states is likely to remain a difficult and complex problem, owing to the fact that these states lie in the transition range between the tight-binding (or atomic) approximation and the effective mass (or free-carrier) approximation. It is nevertheless a useful guide for exploratory work to have even a rough estimate for the energy levels of electrons, providing the concepts are simple. This is particularly true in estimating the nature of electrolyte–semiconductor contacts and the energy levels of gaseous ions on semiconductor surfaces. For example, the charging of the free surface of zinc oxide and of selenium (as used in electrophotography) by ions from a corona in air has provided one of the most effective blocking contacts yet devised. The following discussion makes use of atomic concepts only.

To begin with, we review the physics of ionizing individual atoms. The ionization energy of hydrogen, for example, can be looked upon as the net work required to create new Coulomb fields and energies around the electron and proton extending from an atomic radius to infinity. In the atomic state, the Coulomb fields of electron and proton cancel each other beyond an atomic radius. The net work to create these new Coulomb fields is just half the newly created energy since, by the Virial Theorem, the electron in its ground state has a kinetic energy equal to half its potential energy. Hence, the ionization energy of atoms can, in the hydrogenic approximation, be set equal to the newly created electrostatic energy around the electron and proton minus the kinetic energy of the electron in its ground state in the atom. For most atoms, the first ionization energy lies between 5 and 10 volts.This would correspond to creating a "new" Coulomb field, by the ionization process, extending from about one angstrom to infinity. The electrostatic energy in a Coulomb field is about $7/r$ electron volts when r is measured in angstroms. This brief comment is inserted here to contrast the large role played by Coulomb energies in the ionization of isolated atoms with the minor role it plays in the ionization of atoms in a solid.

9.1 Cohesive Energies, Electron Affinities, and Forbidden Gaps

We review now the binding energies of ionic solids as traditionally presented in discussions of the various types of binding in solids. We define the *cohesive* energy as that energy needed to separate a crystal into its component *atoms*; the *crystal* energy as that energy needed to separate a crystal into its component *ions*; Coulomb energy as the energy in the radial electrostatic field surrounding ions (or electrons); and the energy of electron affinity of atoms as non-Coulombic in the above sense. While the energy of electron affinity is composed of the electrostatic interactions between electrons and between electrons and the positive nucleus, it is derived from short-range forces extending from an ionic radius inward, whereas Coulomb energy by our definition extends from an ionic radius outward. Thus, in assemblies of ions of opposite sign, as in an ionic solid, Coulomb energies are largely destroyed while electron affinities remain largely unaffected.

The cohesive energy is usually written as

$$E_c = -E_I + E_A + E_M \qquad (9.1)$$

where E_I is the ionization energy of the metal atom; E_A, the electron affinity of the electronegative atom (e.g., chlorine);

and E_M the Madelung energy, gained by assembling remote ions into an ionic crystal. It is customary to say that in the case of the alkali halides the first two terms, each about four volts, tend to cancel each other, leaving the Madelung energy of about eight volts as the major "source of binding."

There are certain advantages, as we shall show, in rewriting the terms of equation 9.1 in a form that suggests an alternative interpretation. One has a latitude of interpretation in such problems dictated largely by taste and by the operations of interest. The modified form of equation 9.1 is

$$E_c = E_K - 2E_I + E_M + E_A \qquad (9.2)$$

The ionization energy E_I has been written in the hydrogenic approximation as the sum of a kinetic energy E_K and a purely Coulomb energy $2E_I$. [For hydrogen, $E_K = E_I$.] The terms in equation 9.2 can be separated into the two Coulomb energies, $-2E_I$ and E_M, and the non-Coulomb energies, E_K and E_A. For the alkali halides, the Coulomb energies are largely self canceling, leaving the sum of the electron affinity and the kinetic energy as the major "source of binding." For other ionic solids the first three terms in equation 9.2 are largely self canceling, leaving the electron affinity as the major "source of binding." Insofar as the electron affinity approaches the cohesive energy, the sum of the Coulomb energies in equation 9.2 must be *negative* and hence must "contribute to anti-binding." We use quotation marks as a reminder that these phrases are ways of looking at the various components of the cohesive energy and not unique descriptions.

Table 9.1 shows the cohesive energies of a number of ionic solids and, for comparison, the sums of the electron affinities of the electronegative atoms. For example, for $NiCl_2$, twice the electron affinity of Cl is listed. For all of the ionic solids, the electron affinity is over half the cohesive energy, and for many of them the electron affinity is well over three fourths of the cohesive energy. Also listed in Table 9.1 are some of the forbidden gap energies as taken from a listing by T. S. Moss and

Table 9.1. Heats of Solution, Heats of Formation, Electron Affinities, and Forbidden Gaps[a]

Compound	Heat of solution (From solid)	E_c, Heat of formation (From atomic state)	Sum of electron affinities of negative ions	Electron affinity per negative ion	Approximate forbidden gap
AgI		4.6	3.1	3.1	2.9[b]
AgBr		5.1	3.6	3.6	2.9[b]
AgCl		5.5	3.8	3.8	3.3[b]
BaBr$_2$	0.2	11.9	7.3	3.6	5.5[c]
CaBr$_2$	1.0	12	7.3	3.6	
CaCl$_2$	0.8	12.7	7.6	3.8	
CdI$_2$		5.3	6.3	3.1	3.5[c]
CdBr$_2$	0.02	6.8	7.3	3.6	4.5[c]
CdCl$_2$	0.2	7.6	7.6	3.8	5.5[c]
CoI$_2$		8.5	6.3	3.1	2.5[c]
CoBr$_2$	0.8	9.3	7.3	3.6	2.5[c]
CoCl$_2$	0.8	10.4	7.6	3.8	3.5[c]
CuI		5.3	3.1	3.1	3[d]
CuBr		5.8	3.6	3.6	3[d]
CuCl		6.2	3.8	3.8	3.3[d]
HgI$_2$		3.7	6.3	3.2	2.3[b]
InI		4.7	3.1	3.1	
InCl		5.9	3.8	3.8	2.5[c]
KI	−0.2	5.4	3.1	3.1	(5.6)[e]
KBr	−0.2	6.1	3.6	3.6	(6.6)[e]
KCl	−0.2	6.4	3.8	3.8	(7.6)[e]
NaI	0.05	5.1	3.1	3.1	
NaBr	−0.01	5.9	3.6	3.6	(6.5)[e]
NaCl	−0.05	6.5	3.8	3.8	(7.8)[e]
NiI$_2$		8.3	6.3	3.1	
NiBr$_2$	0.8	8.9	7.3	3.6	3[c]
NiCl$_2$	0.8	10.0	7.6	3.8	4[c]
PbI$_2$		5.9	6.3	3.1	2.4[b]
PbBr$_2$	−0.5	7.2	7.3	3.6	3.2[c]
PbCl$_2$	−0.3	8.1	7.6	3.8	3.8[c]
RbI	−0.3	5.4	3.1	3.1	
RbBr	−0.3	6.1	3.6	3.6	(6.4)[e]
RbCl	−0.2	6.6	3.8	3.8	(7.4)[e]

Table 9.1—Continued

Compound	Heat of solution (From solid)	E_c, Heat of formation (From atomic state)	Sum of electron affinities of negative ions	Electron affinity per negative ion	Approximate forbidden gap
TlI		4.2	3.1	3.1	2.5[c]
TlBr		4.8	3.6	3.6	2.8[c]
TlCl	−0.5	5.2	3.8	3.8	3.2[c]
ZnI₂	0.5	5.5	6.3	3.1	4[c]
ZnCl₂	0.7	8.0	7.6	3.8	

[a] All data are given in electron volts per molecule.
[b] From T. S. Moss, *Proc, Phys. Soc. (London)*, **63**, 167 (1950).
[c] H. Fesefeldt, *Z. Physik*, **64**, 741 (1930).
[d] From S. Nikitine, *Proc. Intern. Conf. Semicond. Phys., Prague*, **1960**.
[e] The values for the alkali halides are for the first exciton peak, which in many cases is near the value for the forbidden gap.

as estimated roughly from thin-film optical transmission data by Fesefeldt. In the case of divalent compounds like NiCl₂, the forbidden gap is to be compared with the electron affinity of one Cl atom (rather than with the sum of the affinities of both atoms), since such a comparison is closer to the optical process of exciting an electron from valence to conduction band. Many of the forbidden gaps are within 20% of the electron affinity of the electronegative atom.

Insofar as the cohesive energy is given by the electron affinity, one can picture the formation of an ionic solid in the following manner (Fig. 9.1). Assemble a group of A and B atoms in a three-dimensional chckerboard array such that A atoms are surrounded by B atoms. Let the B atoms have a larger electron affinity than the A atoms. In a very rough approximation, neglect the energy involved in assembling the *atomic* array. Now, let an electron move from each A to each B atom, forming an ionic crystal. The energy to ionize an A atom is small com-

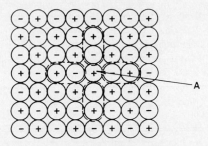

Fig. 9.1. Cancellation of Coulomb field of ions (e.g., A) by "frozen-in polarization" arising from symmetry of ionic solid.

pared with its normal ionization energy since, by the symmetry of the array, the Coulomb energy created per atom is small compared with that created for isolated atoms. It is as if the Coulomb field of each ion is substantially shorn off at its nearest neighbor distance or, as if by the symmetry of the array, the Coulomb field of each ion is "polarized out" beyond the distance of nearest neighbors. This polarization is not derived from the normal dielectric constant of the ionic crystal but rather from a kind of frozen-in polarization formed by the dipoles surrounding each ion (see Fig. 9.1). If we neglect the ionization energy of the A atom, the energy gained by transferring electrons from A to B atoms is just the electron affinity of the B atoms, and this is in large part the cohesive energy of the solid.

In this rough picture of the formation of an ionic solid, the Coulomb energies, ionization and Madelung, play a minor role in the heat of formation from the atomic state. In fact, by transferring the electron in the *solid* array, one short-circuits both the ionization and Madelung energies. It is true that we have neglected the kinetic energy of the valence electrons in assembling the A and B atoms into an *atomic* array. To the extent that in Table 9.1, the electron affinities approach the cohesive energies, this kinetic energy is cancelled by a repulsive Coulomb energy coming from the fact that the transfer of electrons from A to B must build up new Coulomb energies.

In the alkali halides the kinetic energy contributes significantly to the cohesive energy.

The rough correlation between electron affinities, cohesive energies and the energy of the forbidden gap is not confined to

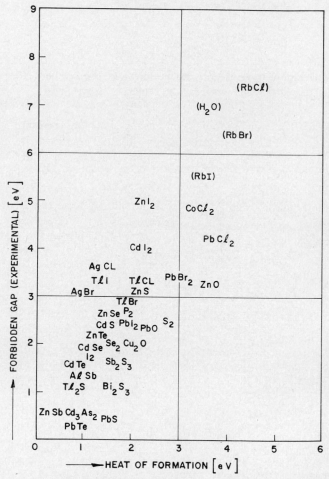

Fig. 9.2. Correlation between forbidden gaps and heats of formation from the normal states of the components.

ionic solids. Figure 9.2 shows the forbidden gap energies of a number of non-ionic as well as ionic solids plotted as a function of their heats of formation starting from their components in their normal states. This is perhaps the simplest correlation one can explore, since these heats of formation are the most readily available. No attempt has been made to refine the correlation by computing the heat of formation from the atomic state.

9.2   Energy Levels in Electrolytes and Solids

Inspection of any of the well-known tables on heats of solution (see Table 9.1) shows that the energy involved in dissolving an ionic solid in water is generally small compared with the heat of formation of the solid and, indeed, often only a few per cent of it. To a physicist schooled in computing the crystal energy of an ionic solid via the Madelung energy, this small heat of solution may be at least transiently surprising. The Madelung energy involves an infinite sum of Coulomb interactions over surrounding ions; it depends in principle on the crystal structure; and it involves the sum of the ionic radii rather than the individual radii separately. It would be natural to expect a significant change in energy when the crystal is dissolved in water so that the ions are now independent of each other, there is no crystal structure, and the sum of ionic radii no longer has significance.

The discussion in Section 9.1 gives an immediate argument for expecting closely the same energies for ions in a solid as for the same ions in water. Starting with ions in free space, the major gain in energy when these ions are combined into a crystal is the destruction of the Coulombic energies beyond an ionic radius. But the major gain in energy when these ions are dropped into water is also the destruction of the same Coulombic energy by the high dielectric constant of water.

We can use the above argument to suggest that the energy levels of electrons on ions in an electrolyte are approximately the same as in an ionic crystal. That is, approximately the same work should be required to transfer an electron from Cl^- to Na^+ in a salt solution as in a crystal. Insofar as this argument is valid, we can compute the energies of electrons in an electrolyte relative to vacuum and use these levels at least as a guide to energy levels in solids and to the electronic behavior of electrolytes and solids in contact.

For example, the electron on a negative chlorine ion in solution lies below vacuum by the sum of the heat of hydration of Cl^- and the electron affinity of Cl. We neglect the heat of solution of neutral chlorine atoms. Similarly, the outer electron of a neutral Na atom in solution lies below vacuum by the ionization energy of Na (in vacuum) *minus* the heat of hydration of Na^+. The heat of solution of neutral Na in the form of neutral sodium atoms is again neglected. In this way, the table in Figure 9.3 was constructed to show the distance in electron volts from vacuum for electrons attached to various atoms or ions in solution. To use this table as a guide to electron energy levels in solids, we note that the position of Na relative to vacuum should be a measure of the electron affinity (distance of conduction band to vacuum) of sodium compounds. Similarly, the distance of Cl^- from vacuum should be a measure of the threshold for photoemission from valence band to vacuum of compounds of chlorine. The forbidden gap of NaCl would then be given by the difference in energy between Na and Cl^- as shown in the table. The table reflects the well-known small affinities of alkali and alkaline earth compounds, the larger electron affinities of compounds of silver, copper, nickel, etc., and the large forbidden gaps of the alkali halides. The deep-lying energies of the halogens shows why these make excellent blocking contacts (in the absence of chemical reactions) to the conduction bands of most solids.

We return to the heat of solution of ionic solids in water to note a simple argument for the lack of solubility of compounds having even a small degree of covalence. The solid must by definition be either ionic or (to some degree) covalent. If the

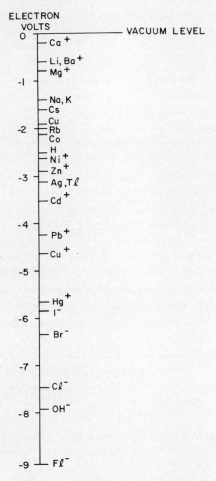

Fig. 9.3. Electronic energy levels derived from heats of hydration.

solid is ionic, it will dissolve in water with little evolution of heat because, as we have noted, the energy of ions in water is closely the same as in the solid. If the solid is to some degree covalent, it is so, logically, because the covalent state represents a lower or deeper energy state than the ionic state. Hence the covalent state will also be deeper than the state of ions in solution. Only a small disparity in this direction is enough to prevent solution of the solid in water. Hence, the presence or absence of solubility depends on small energy differences—small in comparison with the heat of formation.

By this same argument, we can also use the energy gap computed for a compound on the assumption that it is ionic as a first approximation or lower limit to the actual energy gap even where the compound is covalent.

The major emphasis of this chapter is that the transfer of an electron between neighboring atoms in an ionic solid involves predominantly chemical energies in the sense of "valence" and "affinity" concepts rather than coulomb energies as suggested by traditional arguments using the Madelung energy. While the traditional procedure of forming ions from isolated atoms and then bringing them together to form a solid may be a convenient method for computation, it should be borne in mind that this cycle first creates large coulomb energies and then destroys substantially the same coulomb energies in the formation of the solid leaving a net energy that is more "affinity like" than "coulomb like."

References

Fesefeldt, H., *Z. Physik*, **64**, 741 (1930).

Moss, T. S., *Proc. Phys. Soc. (London)*, **63**, 167 (1950),

Nikitine, S., *Proc. Intern. Conf. Semicond. Phys. Prague*, 1960 (pub. 1961), p. 438 (paper K-10).

Ruppel, W., A. Rose, and H. J. Gerritsen, *Helv. Phys. Acta*, **30**, 238 (1957).

Williams, R., *J. Chem. Phys.*, **32**, 1505 (1960).

α	Charge or energy contribution per random event
β	Index of refraction
ΔB	Amplifier passband
C	Capacitance
c	Velocity of light
D	Diffusion constant $[= (kT/e)\mu]$
D_n	Electron $\Big\}$ demarcation levels
D_p	Hole
e	Electronic charge (positive value)
$\mathcal{E}$	Electric field
E_c	Conduction band
E_v	Valence band
E_t	Trap
E_r	Recombination center $\Big\}$ energy level
E_f	Fermi
E_{fn}	Steady-state electron Fermi
E_{fp}	Steady-state hole Fermi
$\lvert E_c, E_{fn} \rvert$	Energy interval (absolute value) between E_c and E_{fn}
E_I	Atomic ionization energy
E_A	Atomic affinity
E_M	Madelung energy
F	Total number of excitations/sec
f	Number of excitations/cm^3-sec
G	Photoconductive gain
h	Planck's constant (6.5×10^{-27} erg-sec)
I	Current

161

I_n — Total *rms* noise current

θ — Ratio of density of free electrons to density of electrons in traps

k — Boltzmann constant

K — Relative dielectric constant

L — Electrode spacing

L_D — Diffusion length

l — Mean free path between collisions

M — Ratio of total anode charge to total number of electrons in thermal contact with the conduction band

m — Free electron mass

$m_e{}^*$ — Effective mass of electrons

$m_h{}^*$ — Effective mass of holes

μ — Mobility

n — Free-electron (optically excited)

p — Free-hole (optically excited)

n_0 — Free-electron (thermally excited)

p_0 — Free-hole (thermally excited)

n_t — Electron-occupied traps — volume

p_t — Hole-occupied traps — density

N_t — Electron-trapping states

P_t — Hole-trapping states

n_r — Electron-occupied recombination center

p_r — Hole-occupied recombination center

N_r — Recombination states $(n_r + p_r)$

$\mathfrak{N}$ — Free electrons

$\mathfrak{N}_t$ — Electron-occupied traps — total

$\mathcal{P}_r$ — Hole-occupied recombination centers — number

ν — Optical frequency

$\nu_n{}^*$ — Electron ⎱ frequency-of-escape factor for thermal

$\nu_p{}^*$ — Hole ⎰ excitation

s_n — Capture cross section of recombination center for free electrons

s_p — Capture cross section of recombination center for free holes

τ	Free-carrier $\Big\rbrace$	
τ_n	Free-electron	lifetime
τ_p	Free-hole	
τ_0	Free-carrier	
τ_{0n}	Free-electron	response time to changes
τ_{0p}	Free-hole	in light intensity
τ_{rel}	Dielectric relaxation time $[K/(4\pi ne\mu)] \times 10^{-12}$	
τ_t	Mean time in conduction band between trapping events	
T_r	Transit time of free carrier between electrodes	
T	Absolute temperature	
T_c	Characteristic temperature used to describe exponential distribution of states	
v	Thermal velocity	
ω	Solid angle	

Index